Learn To Speak™ SPANISH Workbook

THE COMPLETE INTERACTIVE COURSE

Donna Deans Binkowski, Ph.D.
Daniela Melis, M.A.
Based on original content by:
Cynthia Duncan, Ph.D.
Charles J. Bruno, Ph.D.
Martin P. Rice, Ph.D.

HOW TO USE YOUR WORKBOOK

This *Learn To Speak Spanish* Workbook lets you access most of the program's content in printed form, and also allows you to continue to study and practice grammar away from your computer. This book contains:

- Story and Action dialogues from each chapter
- Grammar topics and exercises for each chapter
- An alphabetical index of the vocabulary in *Learn To Speak's* online dictionary

The program will be your principal tool for gaining listening comprehension and conversation skills, but this text can serve as a handy reference tool for vocabulary and grammar questions, as an aid during conversations with the onscreen characters, and as a workbook for reviewing and practicing grammar.

Contents

Part 1: Grammar Topics and Exercises

Part 2: Dialogues and Vocabulary

Chapter 1

GENDER OF NOUNS

In Spanish, all nouns are either masculine or feminine in gender. This is merely a grammatical concept; it does not mean that Spanish speakers perceive things as having male or female attributes. Nouns that refer to male people or animals, and most nouns that end in *-o* are masculine in gender. (One common exception is *la mano,* 'the hand'). Most nouns that refer to female people or animals, and most nouns that end in *-a, -ción, -dad or -tad* are feminine in gender. (Some exceptions are *el día, el problema, el drama, and el programa*). Nouns that have other endings, or nouns that are exceptions to the rules, must be memorized: *el billete, el dólar, el valor,* etc.

DEFINITE AND INDEFINITE ARTICLES

In English, the definite article is 'the,' and the indefinite article is 'a,' or 'an'. In Spanish, the articles have four forms, and they must agree with the noun in number (singular or plural) and gender (masculine or feminine):

	Masculine	**Feminine**
Definite Articles	*el*	*la* (singular)
	los	*las* (plural)
Indefinite Articles	*un*	*una* (singular)
	unos	*unas* (plural)

Examples: *el aeropuerto, los billetes, la empleada, las oficinas, un hombre, unos dólares, una señora, unas conversaciones.*

PLURAL OF NOUNS

Spanish nouns that end in a vowel form plurals by adding the letter *-s.* Nouns that end in a consonant add *-es.* Nouns that end in the consonant *-z* change the *-z* to *-c* before adding *-es*: *el lápiz* ('pencil'), pl. *los lápices.* Nouns that have the last syllable accented in the singular form will lose the accent mark when the noun is plural: *la conversación, las conversaciones; la razón* ('reason'), *las razones,* etc.

As well when the noun is plural the definite and indefinite articles must be used in the plural form: *un hombre>unos hombres*; *la conversación>las conversaciones. Unos* and *unas* mean some, several or a few.

In Spanish, the masculine plural form of a noun is used when referring to a group made up of males and females: *los amigos* (includes both male and female friends).

EXERCISES

Definite and Indefinite Articles

Fill in the blank with the correct definite article from the list:

1. [la; el; los; las] ________ señor
2. [el; los; la; las] ________ señora
3. [el; la; los, las] ________ oficinas
4. [el; los; la; las] ________ billetes
5. [la; los; el; las] ________ dólar
6. [el; la; las, los] ________ pesos
7. [la; el; los; las] ________ cambio
8. [la; el; los; las] ________ oficina de cambio

Plural of Nouns

Draw a line from the noun to the correct indefinite article.

1.	señor	(unos)
2.	señoras	(unas)
3.	oficina de cambio	(unos)
4.	billete	(un)
5.	dólares	(un)
6.	pesos	(una)

Chapter 2

SUBJECT PRONOUNS

The subject pronoun which indicates who is doing the action generally precedes the verb. The forms are:

Singular	**Plural**
(I) yo	(we) nosotros, nosotras
[You (informal)] tú	vosotros, vosotras
[You (formal)] usted	ustedes
(it, he) él	(they) ellos
(it, she) ella	(they) ellas

Nosotros and *vosotros* have feminine forms (*nosotras*, *vosotras*) when referring to a group made up entirely of women. If the group contains both males and females, the masculine form is used. Similarly, *ellos* can refer to a group made up of both men and women, while *ellas* refers to a group made up entirely of females.

THE USE OF SUBJECT PRONOUNS

In English, the subject 'it' is always mentioned: 'it is interesting,' 'here it is,' 'where is it?,' etc. In Spanish, however, the subject pronoun 'it' is rarely, if ever, expressed. The verb stands alone, and the subject 'it' is understood: *Es interestante*, *aquí está*, *¿dónde está*? etc.

Because most verb endings in Spanish tell who is doing the action, it is not necessary to use the subject pronouns in most cases: *Trabajo en esta compañia* (the verb ending *-o* indicates that the subject of the sentence is 'I'). Only when there is a chance of confusion, or if the speaker wants to emphasize who is doing the action, is the subject pronoun used: *Ella es española, pero él es norteamericano* (the verb *es* can have as a subject 'he' and 'she'); *Yo quiero comer ahora* (the *yo* is used only for emphasis, but is not necessary).

THE FORMAL AND INFORMAL 'YOU'

Spanish has two forms of 'you,' the formal (*usted* [Ud.] *ustedes* [Uds.]) and the informal (*tú*, *vosotros*). There are no hard and fast rules for when to use one form or the other but, in general, if you know the person well enough to call him or her by his or her first name, use *tú*. If you address the person by Mr., Miss, or Mrs. with a last name, use *usted* (commonly abbreviated as *Ud.*) If you are unsure about which form to use, it is better to start off with *usted*. The native speaker can suggest that you use *tú* if it is more appropriate.

In Spain, a distinction is made between the plural forms *ustedes* (formal) and *vosotros/vosotras* (informal). In Spanish America, however, *ustedes* is used for both formal and informal situations. Use the plural whenever you are directly addressing more than one person.

EXERCISES

Subject Pronouns

Draw a line to the correct subject pronoun.

1. When speaking about yourself. [yo; tú; usted; él; ella]
2. When speaking about Mr. Smith. [yo; tú; usted; él; ella]
3. When speaking about Mr. and Mrs. Smith. [nosotros; vosotros; ellos; ustedes]
4. When speaking about Mrs. Smith. [yo; tú; usted; él; ella]
5. When speaking about yourself and Mr. Smith. [nosotros; nosotras; ellos; ellas]
6. When speaking about Mrs. Smith and Mrs. Santiago. [nosotros; nosotras; ellas; ellos]
7. When speaking about your friend Thomas. [yo; tú; usted; él; ella]
8. When speaking about your friend Karen. [yo; tú; usted; él; ella]
9. When speaking about the taxi driver. [yo; tú; usted; él; ella]
10. When speaking about Mr. and Mrs. Santiago. [ellos; nosotros; vosotros; ustedes]
11. When speaking about Mrs. Smith and her son. [nosotros; vosotros; ellos; ustedes]
12. When speaking about Mrs. Santiago and her daughter. [nosotros; nosotras; ellos; ellas]
13. When speaking about yourself. [usted; yo; tú; él; ella]
14. When speaking about Mr. Smith. [él; ella; yo; tú; usted]
15. When speaking about Mr. and Mrs. Smith. [nosotros; vosotros; ellos; ustedes]
16. When speaking about Mrs. Smith. [él; ella; yo; tú; usted]
17. When speaking about yourself and Mr. Smith. [nosotros; nosotras; ellos; ellas]
18. When speaking about Mrs. Smith and Mrs. Santiago. [ellos; ellas; nosotros; nosotras]
19. When speaking about your friend Thomas. [tú; usted; ella; él; yo]
20. When speaking about your friend Karen. [yo; tú; usted; él; ella]
21. When speaking about the taxi driver. [él; yo; tú; usted; ella]
22. When speaking about Mr. and Mrs. Santiago. [nosotros; vosotros; ellos; ustedes]
23. When speaking about Mrs. Smith and her son. [ustedes; ellos; nosotros; vosotros]
24. When speaking about Mrs. Santiago and her daughter. [nosotros; nosotras; ellas; ellos]

Formal and Informal Form of "You"

Draw a line to show the appropriate form of "you" to use with the people listed.

1.	tú	Lupe, your maid
2.	ustedes	the agency director, Mrs. García
3.	ustedes	your friends Karen & Silvia
4.	tú	your friend Thomas
5.	usted	your friends Eduardo & Roberto
6.	tú	your friend Elena
7.	ustedes	Mr. and Mrs. Jones
8.	tú	Mrs. Jones and Mrs. García
9.	ustedes	your son
10.	ustedes	your mom and dad
11.	tú	a group of your teachers
12.	usted	the company president
13.	usted	your boss
14.	ustedes	your sister

Chapter 3

PRESENT TENSE INDICATIVE: REGULAR VERBS

In Spanish, all infinitive forms of verbs end in *-ar*, *-er*, or *-ir*. The stem of the verb is the infinitive form less the *-ar*, *-er*, or *-ir* ending. All regular verbs are conjugated in the present tense of the indicative by adding the following personal endings to the stem of the verb:

-AR VERBS

yo	-o
tú	-as
él, ella, Ud.	-a
nosotros(as)	-amos
vosotros(as)	-áis
ellos, ellas, Uds.	-an

-ER VERBS

yo	-o
tú	-es
él, ella, Ud.	-e
nosotros(as)	-emos
vosotros(as)	-éis
ellos, ellas, Uds.	-en

-IR VERBS

yo	-o
tú	-es
él, ella, Ud	-e
nosotros(as)	-imos
vosotros(as)	-ís
ellos, ellas, Uds.	-en

SAMPLE CONJUGATIONS

Hablar (to speak)	*Comer (to eat)*	*Vivir (to live)*
stem: *habl-*	stem: *com-*	stem: *viv-*
yo hablo	como	vivo
tú hablas	comes	vives
él, ella, usted habla	come	vive
nosotros hablamos	comemos	vivimos
vosotros habláis	coméis	vivís
ustedes hablan	comen	viven

MORE ABOUT VERBS

Some common regular verbs ending in *-ar* are:

bailar ('to dance'), *buscar* ('to look for'), *cambiar* ('to change,' 'to exchange'), *comprar* ('to buy'), *desear* ('to want'), *estudiar* ('to study'), *hablar* ('to speak'), *llegar* ('to arrive'), *necesitar* ('to need'), *pagar* ('to pay for'), *preguntar* ('to ask'), *regresar* ('to return'), *tomar* ('to take,' 'to drink'), *trabajar* ('to work').

Some common regular verbs ending in *-er* are:

aprender ('to learn'), *beber* ('to drink'), *comer* ('to eat'), *comprender* ('to understand'), *creer* ('to think'), *leer* ('to read').

Some common regular verbs ending in *-ir* are:

abrir ('to open'), *asistir* ('to attend'), *escribir* ('to write'), *insistir* ('to insist'), *recibir* ('to receive'), *vivir* ('to live').

All of these verbs will follow the patterns you have just learned.

EXERCISES

Present Tense Indicative

Choose the correct subject pronoun for each verb.

1. como [tú; yo; él]
2. vives [ella; nosotros; tú]
3. cambiamos [nosotros; ellos; usted]
4. necesitan [yo; ellos; él]
5. vivimos [ustedes; ella; nosotros]
6. comen [tú; ustedes; nosotros]
7. toma [ellas; yo; él]
8. llevo [yo; usted; ellos]
9. deja [nosotros; ella; yo]
10. paga [tú; usted; nosotros]
11. hablas [ella; ellas; tú]
12. hablan [ellas; usted; tú]

More About Verbs

Fill in the blank with the correct form of the verb.

1. tomar, yo _________
2. llevar, usted _________
3. necesitar, ellos _________
4. cambiar, tú _________
5. hablar, yo _________
6. comer, ustedes _________
7. vivir, ella _________
8. dejar, ellas _________
9. caminar, él _________
10. doblar, tú _________
11. tomar, nosotras _________

Chapter 4

THE VERB "GUSTAR"

The verb *gustar* literally means *to be pleasing* to but it is most commonly translated as *to like* in English. 'I like this hotel' becomes *Me gusta este hotel* (literally, 'This hotel is pleasing to me'). To talk about what other people like or dislike, use the appropriate indirect object pronoun form in front of the verb. To whom is something pleasing?

me (to me)	*nos* (to us)
te (to you [informal])	*os* (to you [informal])
le (to you [formal], to him, to her)	*les* (to you [formal], to him, to her)

When you are describing your own likes and dislikes, use the indirect object pronoun *me* before the verb. Generally, *gustar* is used in just two ways: *gusta* (for one thing that is pleasing) or *gustan* (for more than one thing that is pleasing): *Me gusta el restaurante*; *Me gustan los tacos*. To say that you don't like something, place a *no* in front of the verb: *No me gusta el hotel*; *No me gustan las enchiladas*. Avoid using *gustar* to talk about liking people, as it has sexual connotations in some regions. A more appropriate expression for this will be presented in a later lesson.

What is pleasing? *¿El hotel*? *Me gusta el hotel*, *Te gusta el hotel*, *Le gusta el hotel*, *Nos gusta el hotel*, *Os gusta el hotel*, *Les gusta el hotel*. *¿Los tacos*? *Me gustan los tacos*, *Te gustan los tacos*, *Le gustan los tacos*, *Nos gustan los tacos*, *Os gustan los tacos*, *Les gustan los tacos*. Notice that the verb form, *gusta* or *gustan*, agrees in singular or plural with its grammatical subject, the thing or things that are pleasing, not with the person that is pleased. Finally, when a verb follows *gustar*, it will be in the infinitive: *Me gusta comer tacos*.

ASKING AND ANSWERING "YES / NO" QUESTIONS

A common way to ask a yes/no question in Spanish is simply to change the intonation of your voice by making your voice rise at the end of the question: *¿Usted trabaja en México*? Another way to form a question is to invert the order of the subject and verb, in addition to making your voice rise at the end of the question: *¿Trabaja usted en México*?; *¿Está todo bien*?; *¿Necesita usted algo más*?

To answer a question affirmatively, begin with *Sí* ('yes'): *Sí, trabajo en México*. To answer a question negatively, begin with *No*, and place another *no* in front of the verb: *No, no trabajo en México*.

Notice that the word 'do' from English ('Do you work?') is not translated into Spanish when asking a question.

EXERCISE

The Verb Gustar

Fill in the blank with the correct form of *gustar*.

1. Me ___________ la comida mexicana.
2. ¿Te ___________ las habitaciones?
3. A ellos, les ___________ viajar.
4. Nos ___________ las enchiladas.
5. A ella, no le ___________ los tacos.
6. A Thomas, no le ___________ comer solo.
7. Me ___________ los restaurantes buenos.
8. A nosotros nos ___________ las habitaciones.
9. A ti no te ___________ el desayuno.
10. A los Smith les ___________ el hotel.
11. A mí me ___________ la comida mexicana.
12. A nosotros nos ___________ México.

Chapter 5

NUMBERS 1-100

1 uno
2 dos
3 tres
4 cuatro
5 cinco
6 seis
7 siete
8 ocho
9 nueve
10 diez
11 once
12 doce
13 trece
14 catorce
15 quince
16 dieciséis
17 diecisiete
18 dieciocho
19 diecinueve
20 veinte
21 veintiuno
22 veintidós
23 veintitrés
24 veinticuatro, etc.
30 treinta
31 treinta y uno
32 treinta y dos, etc.
40 cuarenta
41 cuarenta y uno, etc.
50 cincuenta
60 sesenta
70 setenta
80 ochenta
90 noventa
100 cien

NUMBERS ABOVE 100

101 ciento uno/una
200 doscientos/as
300 trescientos/as
400 cuatrocientos/as
500 quinientos/as
600 seiscientos/as
700 setecientos/as
800 ochocientos/as
900 novecientos/as
1.000 mil
2.000 dos mil
1.000.000 un millón

Ciento is used with numbers from 1–99 to express numbers 101–199*: ciento setenta y nueve*, etc. *Cien* is used in counting and before numbers greater than 999: *cien mil*, *cien millones*, etc. When numbers 200–900 precede a noun, they agree in gender: *trescientas habitaciones*, etc. In counting, *mil* does not have a plural form (*tres mil*, *seis mil*) but *millón* does: *dos millones*, *cinco millones*, etc.

WAYS TO EXPRESS POLITE REQUESTS

There are a number of ways to express polite requests in Spanish. For example, you can use a command, accompanied by *por favor* ('please'): *Traígame un café, por favor.* A more polite way of making the same request, however, is to use a form of the verb *querer*: *¿Quiere traerme un café*?; (Literally: 'do you want to bring me a coffee?').

When you want to ask for a favor or make a polite inquiry, you can also use the verb *querer*: *Querría hacer una llamada a los Estados Unidos* ('I would like to make a phone call') OR *Quisiera hacer una llamada a los Estados Unidos* ('I would like to make a phone call').

Sometimes you can use the verb *poder* the same way: *¿Puede usted decirme*? ('Can you tell me?') OR *¿Podría usted indicarme*? ('Could you show me?').

EXERCISES

Numbers Above 100

Write the name of each number in Spanish.

1. 200 ____________________
2. 345 ______________________ _______________ ___ _________
3. 476 ______________________ _______________ ___ _________
4. 510 ______________________ __________
5. 1000 ________________
6. 983 ______________________ _______________ ___ _________
7. 701 ______________________ __________
8. 638 ______________________ _______________ ___ _________
9. 859 ______________________ _______________ ___ _________
10. 267 ______________________ _______________ ___ _________

Ways to Express Polite Requests

Complete the sentence with the proper polite expression.

1. ¿[Perdón; Podría; Gracias] usted decirme dónde hay un buen restaurante?
2. Yo [por favor; puede; quisiera] cambiar cien dólares.
3. Tráigame una cerveza, [por favor; quisiera; lo siento].
4. ¿[Gracias; Puede; Por favor] usted traerme la cuenta, por favor?
5. ¿[Lo siento; Por favor; Podría] usted indicarme dónde está mi habitación?
6. Yo [lo siento; querría; puede] alquilar una habitación.
7. [Gracias; Perdón; Querría], señora. ¿Dónde está el Hotel Plaza?
8. No se marche, [por favor; perdón; podría].
9. Llamaré más tarde, [puede; gracias; por favor].
10. [Querría; Lo siento; Gracias], no contesta nadie.
11. ¿[Quiere; Perdón; Gracias] usted traerme la cuenta, por favor?

Chapter 6

"SER" AND "ESTAR"

Spanish has two verbs that mean 'to be': *ser* and *estar*. Both are irregular in the present tense indicative, and their forms must be memorized.

SER	ESTAR
soy	estoy
eres	estás
es	está
somos	estamos
sois	estáis
son	están

Notice that many forms of *estar* have written accent marks.

SOME USES OF "SER" AND "ESTAR"

Ser and *estar* have numerous uses which you will learn throughout your Spanish studies. *Ser* can be used with many impersonal expressions, such as *es importante*, *es interesante*, *es ridículo*. In addition, some of the common uses of *ser* include:

— to identify a person or a thing

Soy el secretario de la señora Garza.

— to tell time, the day of the week or the date

Hoy es domingo. Es el diez de mayo. Son las nueve de la mañana.

— to express national origin

Nosotros somos de México, pero ellos son de Uruguay.

— to describe the characteristics or traits of a person or thing

María es inteligente. Yo soy tímido. El restaurante es grande, pero bueno.

— to tell what someone does for a living

Antonia es profesora y yo soy ingeniera.

Some comon uses of the verb *estar* are:

— to tell location of a person or thing

Estoy en el restaurante.

— to desribe the emotional or physical condition or someone or something

Octavio y Juan están ocupados. Alicia está bien, pero yo estoy mal.

SOME IRREGULAR VERBS IN THE PRESENT TENSE

Some verbs do not follow the pattern you have learned for present tense verbs, and must be memorized. For example, the *yo* forms of *salir*, *tener*, and *venir* are irregular: *salgo*, *tengo*, and *vengo*. In addition, for other forms of *tener* and *venir* as well as *preferir* and *querer*, when the stem vowel *-e-* is stressed, it becomes *ie*: *tienes*, *vienes*, *prefieres*, *quieres*, and so on. In the same manner, the stem vowel *-o-* in *poder* becomes *ue* when stressed: *puedes*. In vocabulary lists, these changes are listed in parentheses beside the infinitive verb: *preferir* (ie); *poder* (ue), and so on.

TENER (to have)		QUERER (to want)	
tengo	tenemos	quiero	queremos
tienes	tenèis	quieres	querèis
tiene	tienen	quiere	quieren

PODER (to be able)		VENIR (to come)	
puedo	podemos	vengo	venimos
puedes	podèis	vienes	venìs
puede	pueden	viene	vienen

PREFERIR (to prefer)			SALIR (to leave)
prefiero	preferimos	salgo	salimos
prefieres	preferìs	sales	salìs
prefiere	prefieren	sale	salen

EXERCISES

Ser and Estar

Complete the sentence with the correct form of *ser* or *estar*.

1. [Están; Son; Es; Está] las cuatro de la tarde.
2. Thomas y Alberto [es; son; están; está] hombres de negocios.
3. María [están; es; está; son] recepcionista.
4. El restaurante [es; están; está; son] al otro lado de la calle.
5. Thomas [es; está; están; son] en México.
6. Ana y Luisa [está; son; están; es] muy amables.
7. Las maletas no [son; están; es; está] de usted.
8. Elena [está; son; están; es] la esposa de Thomas.
9. Yo [soy; está; estoy; es] bien, gracias.
10. Hola, Roberto. ¿Cómo [estás; eres; estoy; soy]?

Some Uses of Ser and Estar

Fill in the blank with the correct form or *ser* or *estar*.

1. Yo ___________ en el aeropuerto.
2. Nosotros ___________ de los Estados Unidos.
3. Alberto ___________ en una reunión.
4. El apartamento ___________ de Juan.
5. ¿Qué hora ___________?
6. El restaurante ___________ cerca del hotel.
7. ¿___________ todo bien?
8. El hotel ___________ bastante bueno.
9. Los precios ___________ un poco altos.
10. Thomas ___________ muy inteligente.

Irregular Verbs in the Present Tense

Fill in the blank with the correct form of the irregular verb in the present tense.

1. ¿__________ yo reservar una habitación? (poder)
2. ¿__________ ustedes ir al restaurante? (querer)
3. Juan y María ________ del aeropuerto. (salir)
4. Nosotros __________ desde Miami. (venir)
5. Ella _________ de una reunión. (venir)
6. Tú _________ amigos en México. (tener)
7. ¿__________ tú ir al teatro? (querer)
8. Nosotros _______________ comer en el hotel. (preferir)
9. ¿________ yo cambiar unos dólares? (poder)
10. Thomas _________ muchas maletas. (tener)

Chapter 7

INTERROGATIVE WORDS

¿Cómo? (How, what?)

¿Cómo estás? (How are you?)

¿Cómo te llamas? (What is your name?)

¿Dónde? (Where?)

¿Dónde está el hotel? (Where is the hotel?)

¿Qué? (What?)

¿Qué hora es? (What time is it?)

¿Qué es esto? (What is this?)

¿Qué necesita usted? (What do you need?)

¿Cuánto? ¿Cuánta? (How much?)

¿Cuántos? ¿Cuántas? (How many?)

¿Cuántos días? (How many days?)

¿Cuántas personas? (How many people?)

¿Cuándo? (When?)

¿Cuándo llegas? (When do you arrive?)

¿Quién? ¿Quiénes? (Who?)

¿Quién es ella? (Who is she?)

¿Quiénes son ellos? (Who are they?)

¿Cuánto dinero necesitas? (How much money do you need?)

¿Cuántas cervezas quieres comprar? (How many beers do you want to buy?)

CONTRACTIONS "DEL" AND "AL"

In Spanish, there are only two contractions; *del* and *al*, and they are obligatory. Whenever you have the definite article *el* immediately following the preposition *de*, you must make the contraction *del*. Whenever you have the definite article *el* immediately following the preposition *a*, you must make the contraction *al*.

Es el dinero del señor González. (de + el)

Vamos al hotel. (a + el)

Note: "De" and "a" do not contract with any of the other articles.

Es el dinero de la señora García.

Es el dinero de los pasajeros.

Vamos a la oficina.

Vamos a las reuniones.

In Spanish, the word *a* immediately precedes the direct object of a sentence when the direct object refers to a specific person or persons. This personal *a*, which has no equivalent in English, forms contractions in the same manner as the preposition *a*.

Thomas llama a la secretaria.

Thomas llama al secretario.

Voy a ver a la señora Garcia.

Voy a ver al señora Garcia.

MORE IRREGULAR VERBS IN THE PRESENT TENSE

These verbs are commonly used and, since they do not follow the pattern you have learned for regular verbs, they must be memorized.

IR (to go)	voy	vamos	vas	vais	va	van
DAR (to give)	doy	damos	das	dais	da	dan
TRAER (to bring)	traigo	traemos	traes	traéis	trae	traen
PONER (to put)	pongo	ponemos	pones	ponéis	pone	ponen
DECIR (to tell, say)	digo	decimos	dices	decís	dice	dicen
OIR (to hear)	oigo	oímos	oyes	oís	oye	oyen

EXERCISES

Interrogative Words

Fill in the blank with the correct interrogative word.

1. ¿_____________ es ese hombre?
2. ¿_____________ dinero necesitas?
3. ¿_____________ te llamas?
4. ¿_____________ llega Thomas?
5. ¿_____________ cuesta la habitación?
6. ¿_____________ son esas personas?

Contractions Del and Al

Choose the correct form of the preposition and article.

1. Voy [a la; al] aeropuerto.
2. Vengo [del; de la] hotel
3. Thomas llamas [al; a la] secretaria.
4. ¿Me lleva [al; a la] hotel?
5. Juan sale [del; de la] oficina.
6. Voy a ver [al; a la] señor García.
7. El restaurante está [a la; al] otro lado de la calle.

More Irregular Verbs in the Present Tense

Complete the sentence with the correct form of the irregular verb in the present tense.

1. Yo _____________ a mi habitación. (ir)
2. ¿Dónde _____________ (nosotros) el equipaje? (poner)
3. ¿_____________ tú las maletas? (traer)
4. El botones _____________ el equipaje. (traer)
5. El botones _____________ el equipaje al lado de la cama. (poner)
6. Karen le _____________ una propina al botones. (dar)
7. Yo no _____________ nada. (oir)
8. ¿Qué _____________ tú? (decir)
9. Ellas _____________ a cenar al restaurante. (ir)
10. Yo te _____________ mi número de teléfono. (dar)

Chapter 8

SOME USEFUL PREPOSITIONS

cerca de (near, close to)

lejos de (far, far from)

antes de (before)

después de (after)

encima de (on top of)

debajo de (below)

delante de (in front of)

entre (between)

durante (during)

a la izquierda de (to the left of)

a la derecha de (to the right of)

frente a (facing)

en frente de (in front of)

detrás de (behind)

In Spanish, the pronouns that follow prepositions are the same as the subject pronouns, except for first and second person singular forms: *mí, ti*. *Es para mí, es para ti, es para ella, es para ustedes*, etc. One exception to this is the expression 'between you and me,' *entre tú y yo*. The forms *conmigo* ('with me') and *contigo* ('with you' informal singular) are irregular and must be memorized.

"PEDIR" VS. "PREGUNTAR"

Both *pedir* and *preguntar* mean 'to ask' but they are not interchangeable. *Preguntar* means 'to ask a question': *Roberto le pregunta dónde está la oficina* ('Roberto asks her where the office is'). *Pedir* means 'to ask for something,' and is also used to mean 'to order' (in a restaurant): *Roberto le pide información* ('Roberto asks her for information'). *Roberto pide los tacos* ('Roberto orders tacos').

Pedir is slightly irregular, and should be memorized.

PEDIR (to ask for, to order)	pido	pedimos	pides	pedís	pide	piden

"HACER"

The verb *hacer* is irregular in the present tense. You must memorize it.

HACER (to make, to do)	hago	hacemos	haces	hacéis	hace	hacen

Remember that the word 'do' in English questions such as 'Do you speak Spanish?' is not translated into Spanish: *¿Habla usted español*? The verb *hacer* is used to ask the question *¿Qué hace usted*? ('What are you doing?'), but the answer to this question generally involves a verb other than *hacer*: *Leo un libro* ('I'm reading a book'), etc. Answer with *hacer* only when you are actually making something: *Hago un pastel* ('I'm making a cake').

EXERCISES

Pedir vs. Preguntar

Fill in the blank with the correct form of *pedir* or *preguntar*.

1. Thomas le _____________ a una señora dónde está la oficina de correos.
2. El recepcionista le _____________ veinticinco pesos por la habitación.
3. El camarero le _____________ qué quiere comer.
4. La policia le _____________ el pasaporte.
5. Karen le _____________ al botones dónde hay un restaurante.
6. Thomas _____________ agua mineral con la cena.
7. Karen _____________ cerveza con la cena.
8. Mario le _____________ al camarero si tienen tacos.

Hacer

Complete the sentence with the correct subject pronoun.

1. [Tú; Yo; Ella] hago una llamada a larga distancia.
2. [Ud.; Tú; Ella] haces una reservación en el hotel.
3. Thomas necesita marcar "6" cuando [nosotros; él; yo] hace una llamada local.
4. [Nosotros; Uds.; Tú] hacemos un viaje a Acapulco.
5. [Ud.; Uds.; Yo] hace muchas llamadas a los Estados Unidos.
6. [Tú; Ella; Nosotros] hace una reservación a nombre de "Karen Santiago".
7. [Nosotros; Tú; Uds.] hacen varias llamadas a su oficina.

Chapter 9

ORDINAL NUMBERS

primer(o)	first	*sexto*	sixth
segundo	second	*séptimo*	seventh
tercer(o)	third	*octavo*	eighth
cuarto	fourth	*noveno*	ninth
quinto	fifth	*décimo*	tenth

Ordinal numbers are adjectives and must agree with the noun they describe: *la octava semana*, *el sexto piso*, *el cuarto día*, *la primera semana*, etc. Notice that *primero* and *tercero* drop off the *-o* when they precede a masculine noun: *el primer día*, *el tercer día*.

Generally speaking, ordinal numbers above ten are not commonly used in Spanish. You will hear native speakers say instead, *el piso (número) veinte, la lección (número) catorce* and so forth.

INDIRECT OBJECT PRONOUNS

The indirect object of a sentence usually answers the question 'to whom?' or 'for whom?': *Roberto me da un regalo* ('Roberto gives a present to me'); *Yo te compro este libro* ('I'll buy this book for you). To replace the indirect object noun with a pronoun, you must choose the correct form that corresponds to the noun:

me	to me	*nos*	to us
te	to you, informal	*os*	to you all, informal
le	to you, formal	*les*	to you all, formal
le	to him, to her	*les*	to them

Sometimes native speakers will use *le* or *les* as both the direct and indirect object pronoun when they are referring to a male person. If you are not sure which form to use (*le* or *lo*) when talking about a man, you can almost always use *le*.

"MUCHO," "MUY" AND "POCO"

Mucho ('a lot,' 'many') and *poco* ('a few,' 'few') can be either adjectives or adverbs. An adjective modifies a noun, while an adverb usually modifies a verb, adjective, or another adverb. When they are adjectives, they precede the noun, and they have four forms reflecting number and gender: *mucho*, *mucha*, *muchos*, *muchas*, etc. For example, *mucha (poca) cerveza*, *muchos (pocos) hombres*, *mucho (poco) dinero*, *muchas (pocas) amigas*. To express very large or small amounts of something, use *muchísimo* and *poquísimo*.

When *mucho* and *poco* are adverbs, they do not change form. They generally follow the verb, and mean 'very much' or 'very little': *Roberto trabaja mucho (poco).*

Muy is an adverb. It means 'very': *muy rápido, muy interestante, muy bien.* Never use *muy* with *mucho.* To express very large or very small amounts of something, use *muchísimo/a* and *poquísimo/a.*

EXERCISES

Indirect Object Pronoun

Choose the correct indirect object pronoun.

1. Hablo con la operadora. = [Me; Le; Les] hablo.
2. Ella da la dirección a mí. = Ella [te; me; le] da la dirección.
3. Traigo una cerveza a ti. = [Nos; Te; Me] traigo una cerveza.
4. El camarero llama a nosotros. = El camarero [os; nos; les] llama.
5. Hago un precio especial a ustedes. = [Les; Le; Nos] hago un precio especial.
6. Pregunto a Karen qué quiere comer. = [Te; Le; Me] pregunto qué quiere comer.
7. El camarero da el menú a ellos. = El camarero [nos; le; les] da el menú.

Mucho, Muy, and Poco

Complete the sentence with the correct adverb or adjective.

1. La comida es ____________ buena.
2. Hay ____________ gente en el aeropuerto.
3. Thomas trabaja ____________.
4. El hotel es ____________ caro.
5. México es una ciudad ____________ grande.
6. Es una ciudad ____________ interesante.
7. Yo no tengo ____________ dinero.
8. ____________ personas viven en Latinoamérica.
9. Karen tiene ____________ amigos en México.
10. Thomas toma ____________ café.

Chapter 10

GREETINGS AND POLITE EXPRESSIONS

Buenos días.
Good morning, Good day.

Buenas tardes.
Good afternoon.

Buenas noches.
Good evening, Good night.

¡Hola!
Hi!

¿Cómo está usted?
How are you? (formal)

¿Cómo estás?
How are you? (informal)

¿Qué tal estás?
How are you? (informal)

¿Qué tal?
What's going on? How are things?

Muy bien, gracias.
Very well, thank you.

Adiós. Hasta luego.
Good-bye. Until later.

Hasta mañana.
Until tomorrow.

Muchas gracias.
Thanks very much.

De nada.
You're welcome.

Por favor.
Please.

Perdón. Con permiso.
Excuse me. Pardon me.

INTRODUCING PEOPLE

INFORMAL

Antonio, ¿conoces a mi amigo, Paco?
Antonio, do you know my friend, Paco?

Antonio, quiero presentarte a mi amigo, Paco.
Antonio, I'd like to introduce you to my friend, Paco.

Hola. ¿Qué tal?
Hi, how are you doing?

FORMAL

Sr. Rodríguez, permítame presentarle a mi socio, Santiago Silva
Mr. Rodríguez, allow me to introduce you to my partner, Santiago Silva.

Sra. Silva, le presento a la Sra. Rodríguez.
Mrs. Silva, I'd like you to meet Mrs. Rodríguez.

Mucho gusto.
It's a pleasure to meet you.

El gusto es mío.
The pleasure is mine.

SABER VS. *CONOCER*

Both *saber* and *conocer* mean 'to know,' but they are not used interchangeably. *Saber* is 'to know' information (*No sé el número de teléfono*; *¿Sabe usted dónde está el restaurante*?), or 'to know how' to do something (*No sabemos conducir*). *Conocer* is 'to know' a person (*Conozco a la Sra. García*; *¿Conoces a mi hermana?*), or 'to be familiar with' a place or a thing (*No conocen la ciudad*). Both verbs are irregular and must be memorized.

SABER		CONOCER	
sé	sabemos	conozco	conocemos
sabes	sabéis	conoces	conocéis
sabe	saben	conoce	conocen

EXERCISE

Saber vs. Conocer

Complete the sentence with the correct of form of *saber* or *conocer*.

1. ¿[Sabes; Conoces] a mi hermano?
2. No [sé; conozco] dónde está la estación.
3. ¿[Conocen; Saben] ustedes el nombre de ese señor?
4. Los Smith no [saben; conocen] Colombia.
5. ¿[Sabes; conoces] manejar?
6. Juan [conoce; sabe] a todo el mundo aquí.
7. No [sé; conozco] la ciudad.

Chapter 11

AGREEMENT OF ADJECTIVES

Adjectives of nationality and adjectives that end in *-o* have four forms in Spanish to reflect gender (masculine, feminine) and number (singular, plural). The adjective must agree in gender and number with the noun it describes: *el hombre mexicano, la mujer mexicana, los hombres mexicanos, las mujeres mexicanas, un hotel bueno, una cerveza buena, unos hoteles buenos, unas cervezas buenas*, etc.

Adjectives that end in *-e* or in a consonant have only two forms; singular and plural. These adjectives do not normally reflect gender: *un hombre interesante, una mujer interesante, unos hombres interesantes, unas mujeres interesantes, un precio especial, una comida especial, unos precios especiales, unas comidas especiales.*

PLACEMENT OF ADJECTIVES

Adjectives that describe the qualities of a noun (what something or someone is like) generally follow the noun in Spanish: *un precio especial, un hotel bueno, una mujer inteligente*, etc. Adjectives of quantity and demonstrative adjectives precede the noun: *cinco habitaciones, muchos taxis, pocas personas, otro día, este día, esta noche.*

Occasionally, you will notice that native speakers change some of these rules. For example, you may sometimes hear a native speaker place a descriptive adjective in front of the noun: *un nuevo chofer, un buen día, unos excelentes hoteles.* These changes are for stylistic purposes and only slightly alter the meaning, placing more emphasis on the adjective than usual. An exception to this is *grande.* Before a noun, *grande* becomes *gran*, and means 'important' or 'great.'

THE PRESENT PROGRESSIVE

The present progressive is formed in Spanish by using a conjugated form of the verb *estar* and a gerund. The gerunds are formed for verbs ending in *-ar* by adding *-ando* to the stem; for verbs ending in *-er* or *-ir*, add *-iendo* to the stem: *hablando, bailando, trabajando, comiendo, viviendo, diciendo*, etc. When an unstressed *-i-* occurs between two vowels, it becomes a *-y-*: *leer* > *leyendo*; *creer* > *creyendo*, etc.

Study these examples: *Roberto está trabajando*; *Thomas está comiendo; Ellos están hablando*; *Nosotros estamos preguntando*; *Tú estás viviendo en un hotel...* etc. You will occasionally find this structure used in the dialogues and settings, but you should keep in mind that the present progressive is not as common in Spanish as it is in English. The simple present tense (*trabajo*, *estudio*, etc) is used more frequently to indicate actions in progress.

EXERCISES

Agreement of Adjectives

Choose the correct form of the adjective.

1. La habitación es [pequeño; pequeña; pequeños; pequeñas].
2. Los niños están [animado; animados; animadas; animada].
3. La información es [correcto; correcta; correctos; correctas].
4. La señora está [encantado; encantadas; encantados; encantada] de conocerte.
5. Los cuartos son [grande; grandes].
6. El hotel es [cara; caro; caros; caras].
7. La comida es [buena; bueno; buenas; buenos].

The Present Progressive

Complete the sentence with the correct gerund to form the present progressive.

1. Juan está ____________ por teléfono. (hablar)
2. Nosotros estamos ____________ en la Argentina. (trabajar)
3. Thomas y Elena están ____________ en un hotel. (vivir)
4. Yo estoy ____________ un libro muy interesante. (leer)
5. Silvia está ____________ una carta. (escribir)
6. ¿Por quá estás ____________ tanto café? (beber)
7. Tus amigos están ____________. (bailar)

Chapter 12

TELLING TIME

To ask what time it is in Spanish, ask *¿Qué hora es*? To ask at what time something will happen, ask *¿A qué hora....*?

Use the verb *ser* to tell the time. 'One o'clock' and any variation of one o'clock will use the singular form of the verb, *es*: *Es la una, es la una y diez, es la una y media*. With all numbers above one, use *son*: *Son las dos, son las nueve, son las once y veinte*, etc. Past the half hour, you should go to the next hour and subtract the minutes (3:50 = 'It's ten to four' = *Son las cuatro menos diez*).

The word *media* means 'half,' and *cuarto* means a 'quarter'. *Son las cinco y media* (5:30), *son las nueve y cuarto* (9:15), *son las once menos cuarto* (10:45). Other useful expressions are *en punto* ('on the dot'), *de la mañana* ('A.M.'), *de la tarde* ('P.M.') or *de la noche* ('P.M.'), *la medianoche* ('midnight'), and *el mediodía* ('noon').

HOW TO TALK ABOUT THE FUTURE

There are many ways you can talk about the future in Spanish. The easiest is to use an adverbial phrase indicating a future time (such as *mañana*, *más tarde*, *luego*, *a la(s)* + time, and so on) with the present tense of the verb: *mañana voy al aeropuerto* ('tomorrow I'm going to the airport'); *luego hablamos por teléfono* ('we'll talk on the telephone later'); *a las cinco nos encontramos en la oficina de correos* ('at five o'clock we'll meet at the post office').

Another way to talk about the future is with the future tense. The future tense in Spanish is formed by adding the endings *-é*, *-ás*, *-á*, *-emos*, *-éis*, *-án* to the entire infinitive. Study these examples:

HABLAR	COMER	VIVIR
hablaré	comeré	viviré
hablarás	comerás	vivirás
hablará	comerá	vivirá
hablaremos	comeremos	viviremos
hablaréis	comeréis	viviréis
hablarán	comerán	vivirán

You have already seen another very common way to talk about the future; using the verb *ir* in a conjugated form in the present tense, followed by the preposition *a* and an infinitive: *voy a comer* ('I am going to eat'; 'I will eat'); *vas a comer*, *va a comer*, *vamos a comer*, *vais a comer*, *van a comer*, etc. This structure is especially common in spoken Spanish.

DAYS OF THE WEEK

Los días de la semana:

el lunes	Monday; on Monday
el martes	Tuesday; on Tuesday
el miércoles	Wednesday; on Wednesday
el jueves	Thursday; on Thursday
el viernes	Friday; on Friday
el sábado	Saturday; on Saturday
el domingo	Sunday; on Sunday

Notice that the days of the week in Spanish are not capitalized. When you want to indicate that something happens every Monday, every Saturday, etc., use the plural form of the article: *los lunes*, *los sábados*, etc. Note: On the Hispanic calendar, the first day of the week is Monday.

Other useful phrases: *mañana* ('tomorrow'), *pasado mañana* ('day after tomorrow'), *hoy* ('today'), *esta noche* ('tonight').

EXERCISE

Days of the Week

Fill in the blank with the correct day of the week.

1. El primer día de la semana es el _________.
2. El martes es el día antes del _________.
3. El _________.es el séptimo día.
4. El cuarto día es el _________.
5. El _________.está entre el lunes y el miércoles.
6. El _________.es el sexto día de la semana.
7. El _________.va después del jueves.

Chapter 13

NEGATIVE AND INDEFINITE WORDS

nada	nothing	*algo*	something
nadie	no one	*alguien*	someone
ningún	no, none	*algún*	some, any
ninguno/a	no, none	*alguno/a/os/as*	some, any
nunca	never	*siempre*	always
tampoco	neither	*también*	also
ni... ni	neither nor	*o... o*	either or

Spanish uses a double negative with *no* preceding the verb, and a negative word following the verb: *No conozco a nadie* (literally, I don't know no one'); *No trabajo nunca*; *No hablo francés tampoco*; *No tengo nada*, etc. In addition, to answer a 'yes-no' question in the negative, you would use another *no*: *Necesita usted algo*?— *No, no necesito nada.*

Note that before a masculine singular noun, *ninguno* and *alguno* drop the final *-o* and take a written accent on the *u*: *ningún taxi*, *algún restaurante*, but *ninguna cajera*, *de ninguna manera* ('no way').

STEM-CHANGING VERBS: PRESENT TENSE

Some of the verbs we have introduced as irregular in *Chapter 6* are actually stem-changing verbs. This means that there is a small spelling change in the stem of the verb. However, these verbs do follow a pattern:

e > ie		o or u > ue	
PENSAR (to think)		VOLVER (to return)	
pienso	pensamos	vuelvo	volvemos
piensas	pensáis	vuelves	volvéis
piensa	piensan	vuelve	vuelven

e > i (*ir* verbs only)

PEDIR (to ask for)

pido	pedimos
pides	pedís
pide	piden

Notice that the *nosotros* and *vosotros* forms of the verbs do not have stem changes, whereas the others do.

MORE STEM-CHANGING VERBS

e > ie

cerrar (to close)

empezar (to begin)

pensar (to think)

perder (to lose)

preferir (to prefer [*Ch. 6*])

querer (to want [*Ch. 6*])

e > i

pedir (to ask for)

servir (to serve)

o or u > ue

almorzar (to eat lunch)

dormir (to sleep)

jugar (to play (games))

poder (to be able)

volver (to return [*Ch. 6*])

EXERCISE

Stem-Changing Verbs

Complete the sentence with the correct form of the verb.

1. La oficina se __________ a las cuatro. (cerrar)
2. Yo __________ comer la ensalada. (preferir)
3. ¿Cuándo __________ a tu país? (volver)
4. ¿Cuándo __________ ustedes a visitarnos? (venir)
5. Nosotros no __________ terminar toda la comida. (poder)
6. Thomas __________ el menú. (pedir)
7. Karen y Mario __________ al tenis. (jugar)

Chapter 14

SOME IDIOMS WITH *TENER*

An idiom is an expression that cannot be translated literally from one language to another. A number of idioms in Spanish involve the verb *tener*, and must be memorized.

tener ...años	to be ...years old
tener hambre	to be hungry
tener sed	to be thirsty
tener frío	to be cold
tener calor	to be hot
tener prisa	to be in a hurry
tener sueño	to be sleepy
tener razón	to be right
no tener razón	to be wrong
tener miedo (de)	to be afraid of
tener ganas (de)	to feel like (doing something)
tener que + infinitive	to have to (do something)

REFLEXIVE VERBS AND REFLEXIVE PRONOUNS

A number of verbs in Spanish are reflexive, and are always used with a reflexive pronoun. The pronoun form corresponds to, or reflects the subject (the person doing the action), and immediately precedes the conjugated verb.

MARCHARSE

(yo) me marcho	(nostros/as) nos marchamos
(tú) te marchas	(vosotros/as) os marcháis
(Ud., él, ella) se marcha	(Uds., ellos, ellas) se marchan

The rules about the placement of reflexive pronouns are the same as the rules you have learned about the placement of indirect object pronouns.

SOME COMMON REFLEXIVE VERBS

acostarse (ue)	to go to bed
levantarse	to get up
afeitarse	to shave
llamarse	to be named (called)
bañarse	to take a bath
ponerse	to put on (clothes)
despertarse (ie)	to wake up
quitarse	to take off (clothes)
divertirse (ie)	to enjoy oneself
sentarse	to sit down
dormirse (ue)	to fall asleep
sentirse (ie)	to feel
lavarse	to wash (oneself)
vestirse (i)	to get dressed

Notice that the infinitive always shows *-se* attached to the end of a reflexive verb. When you conjugate the verb, remember to make the pronoun form correspond to the person doing the action: *dormirse* (ue) > *me duermo, te duermes, se duerme, nos dormimos, os dormís, se duermen.*

(Remember that the vowels in parentheses (ue) (ie), etc. indicate that the verb has a stem change. [For a review of stem-changing verbs, see the corresponding section in *Chapter 13*.])

EXERCISES

Reflexive Verbs and Pronouns

Choose the correct reflexive pronoun.

1. Nosostros [nos; os] marchamos.
2. Él [lo; se] acuesta muy tarde.
3. Ellos [os; se] lavan las manos.
4. Tú [te; ti] vistes rápidamente.
5. Ellas [las; se] divierten en la fiesta.
6. Ustedes [se; nos] sienten mal.
7. Usted [los; se] afeita por la mañana.
8. Yo [me; mí] duermo a las diez de la noche.

Some Common Reflexive Verbs

Fill in the blank with the correct form of the reflexive verb.

1. Yo normalmente ___________ a las seis. (despertarse)
2. Entonces, yo ___________ a las seis y me baño. (levantarse)
3. ¿Cómo ___________ ese señor? (llamarse)
4. Roberto ___________ mucho en la fiesta. (divertirse)
5. ¿A qué hora ___________ los niños? (acostarse)
6. ¿No ___________ bien tú? (sentirse)
7. Nosotros ___________ aquí. (sentarse)
8. Tú siempre ___________ en las reuniones. (dormirse)
9. Eduardo ___________ una camisa blanca. (ponerse)
10. Yo ___________ antes de salir de la casa. (vestirse)

Chapter 15

FORMAL COMMANDS

When you are directly addressing a person or persons that you would normally address as *usted* or *ustedes*, give formal commands by taking the *yo* form of the present indicative tense and changing the ending of *-ar* verbs to *-e* for singular (*usted*) commands, or *-en* for plural (*ustedes*) commands and changing the ending of *-er*/*-ir* verbs to *-a* or *-an*. Because you are working from the *yo* form of the present indicative, the formal commands reflect the irregularities you find in irregular and stem-changing verbs.

Regular Verbs

-AR	-ER/-IR
buscar > busque, busquen*	comer > coma, coman
dejar > deje, dejen	insistir > insista, insistan
hablar > hable, hablenleer > lea, lean	
llamar > llame, llamen	vivir > viva, vivan

Verbs with Irregular *yo* Forms

conocer (conozco)>conozca, conozcan	salir (salgo)>salga, salgan
decir (digo)>diga, digan	tener (tengo) >tenga, tengan
oír (oigo)>oiga, oigan	traer (traigo)>traiga, traigan
poner (pongo)>ponga, pongan	venir (vengo)>venga, vengan

Stem-Changing Verbs

almorzar (ue) > almuerce, almuercen*	pedir (i) > pida, pidan
cerrar (ie) > cierre, cierren	perder (ie) > pierda, pierdan
empezar (ie) > empiece, empiecen	servir (i) > sirva, sirvan
jugar (ue) > juegue, jueguen*	volver (ue) > vuelva, vuelvan

* A spelling change is necessary to preserve the sound of the infinitives that end in *-car*, *-gar*, and *-zar*: *c* > *qu*, *g* > *gu*, and *z* > *c*.

A few verbs have irregular command forms and must be memorized:

dar > dé, den	saber > sepa, sepan
estar > esté, estén	ser > sea, sean
ir > vaya, vayan	

FORMATION OF THE PRESENT SUBJUNCTIVE REGULAR VERBS

To form the present subjunctive of most verbs, add the personal endings of the present subjunctive to the *yo* form of the present indicative minus the *-o* ending. For the subjunctive, *-ar* verb endings are *-e*, *-es*, *-e*, *-emos*, *-éis*, *-en*, and *-er* / *-ir* verb endings are *-a*, *-as*, *-a*, *-amos*, *-áis*, *-an*. (Notice that the third person forms [*él/ella/usted* and *ellos/ellas/ustedes*] of regular verbs in the subjunctive are the same forms used in formal commands.)

-ar verbs		-er verbs	
HABLAR		COMER	
hable	hablemos	coma	comamos
hables	habléis	comas	comáis
hable	hablen	coma	coman

-ir verbs	
VIVIR	
viva	vivamos
vivas	viváis
viva	vivan

Just as for the formal commands, since the form of the present subjunctive is taken from the *yo* form of the present indicative, stem-changing verbs and verbs that are irregular in the *yo* form have the same irregularity in the present subjunctive. In addition, verbs ending in *-car*, *-gar*, and *-zar* have the same spelling change that you learned for the formal commands: *c* > *qu*, *g* > *gu*, and *z* > *c*. (See the previous list of irregular and stem-changing verbs for the formal commands if you need to review these.)

The verbs that are irregular for the formal commands are also irregular for the present subjunctive. These forms must be memorized.

PRESENT SUBJUNCTIVE FORMS - IRREGULAR VERBS

These verbs are irregular in the present subjuntive and must be memorized:

DAR		ESTAR	
dé	demos	esté	estemos
des	deis	estés	estéis
dé	den	esté	estén

HABER		SABER	
haya	hayamos	sepa	sepamos
hayas	hayáis	sepas	sepáis
haya	hayan	sepa	sepan

IR	
vaya	vayamos
vayas	vayáis
vaya	vayan

EXERCISES

Formal Commands

Choose the correct form of the verb to make a formal command.

1. [Habla; Hablen; Hable; Hablan] usted más despacio, por favor.
2. [Esperan; Esperen; Espere; Espera] ustedes junto a la puerta.
3. [Llamen; Llame; Llama; Llaman] usted más tarde.
4. [Vayan; Van; Va; Vaya] ustedes hasta la calle siguiente.
5. [Trae; Traigan; Traiga; Traen] usted la cuenta, por favor.
6. [Salen; Salga; Salgan; Sale] ustedes del autobús con cuidado.
7. [Pone; Ponga; Pongan; Ponen] usted almidón en las camisas.

Present Subjunctive Forms

Fill in the blank with the correct form of the verb.

1. Quiero que usted __________ la ropa en agua fría. (lavar)
2. Quiero que ustedes __________ a verme hoy. (venir)
3. Prefiero que los niños no __________ solos en la casa. (estar)
4. Es necesario que tú me __________ tu número de teléfono. (dar)
5. Espero que alguien __________ el teléfono. (contestar)
6. Les recomiendo que ustedes no __________ el agua. (beber)
7. ¿Qué quieres que yo __________ ahora? (hacer)
8. Quiero que tú me __________ toda la verdad. (decir)

Chapter 16

PRETERITE OF REGULAR VERBS

The preterite is a past tense in Spanish. It is used for actions that are COMPLETED in the past. The preterite endings are added to the stem of the infinitive (*habl-*, *com-*, *viv-*). Notice the *-er* and *-ir* verbs have the same endings in the preterite.

-ar verbs	-er verbs	-ir verbs
HABLAR	COMER	VIVIR
hablé	comí	viví
hablaste	comiste	viviste
habló	comió	vivió
hablamos	comimos	vivimos
hablasteis	comisteis	vivisteis
hablaron	comieron	vivieron

Note: *Ver* has no accents in the preterite: *vi*, *viste*, *vio*, *vimos*, *visteis*, *vieron*.

SOME SPELLING CHANGES IN THE PRETERITE

Verbs that have stem changes in the present tense do not have the same change in the preterite. Verbs ending in *-ar* or *-er* have no stem change in the preterite: *pensar (ie)* > *pensé*, *pensaste*, *pensó*, *pensamos*, etc.; *volver (ie)* > *volví*, *volviste*, *volvió*, *volvimos*, etc.

Verbs ending in *-ir* do have a stem change in the preterite, but only in the third person singular and plural. This change is not always the same change as for the present tense. In vocabulary lists, stem changes for the preterite are listed in parentheses next to the stem change information for the present tense.

DORMIR (ue, u)

dormí, *dormiste*, *durmió*, *dormimos*, *dormisteis*, *durmieron*

PEDIR (i, i)

pedí, *pediste*, *pidió*, *pedimos*, *pedisteis*, *pidieron*

Verbs ending in *-car*, *-gar*, and *-zar* have a spelling change in the first person singular of the verb, where *c* > *qu*, *g* > *gu*, and *z* > *c*. Recall that a similar spelling change occurs for these verbs in the formal commands and in the present subjunctive.

buscar > busqué

pagar > pagué

empezar > empecé

Verbs ending in two unstressed vowels have a spelling change in the third person singular and plural.

creer > creyó, creyeron

leer > leyó, leyeron

caer > cayó, cayeron

SOME IRREGULAR VERBS IN THE PRETERITE

There are many verbs that are irregular in the preterite. Their forms must be memorized.

DAR
di, diste, dio, dimos, disteis, dieron

IR
fui, fuiste, fue, fuimos, fuisteis, fueron

SER
fui, fuiste, fue, fuimos, fuisteis, fueron

The rest of the irregular verbs share the preterite endings *-e*, *-iste*, *-o*, *-imos*, *-isteis*, *-ieron*. Notice that none of the endings have accent marks. For these verbs you can learn the irregular preterite stem and use the appropriate endings. Note: The third person singular form of *hacer* has a spelling change of *c* > *z*: *hizo*. Also, the third person plural form of *decir* and *traer* does not use the *-i-* of the ending: *dijeron*, *trajeron*.

hacer > hic-

estar > estuv-

tener > tuv-

poder > pud-

poner > pus-

querer > quis-

saber > sup-

venir > vin-

decir > dij-

traer > traj-

EXERCISES

Preterite of Regular Verbs

Choose the correct subject pronoun.

1. El año pasado [tú; ella; yo] visité Chile.
2. ¿Hablaste [nosotros; tú; él] con el farmacéutico?
3. [Nosotros; Ellos; Tú] vivieron dos años en el Perú.
4. [Nosotros; Thomas; Yo] bebió una cerveza.
5. [Tú; Uds.; Yo] nunca comiste en ese restaurante.
6. ¿Reservó [yo; usted; nosotros] una mesa en el restaurante?
7. [Ella; Yo; Tú] te vi con Eduardo anoche.
8. ¿Consultó [tú; usted; yo] a un médico?

Spelling Changes in the Preterite

Fill in the blank with the correct preterite form of the verb.

1. Nosotros __________ al mar. (ir)
2. Roberto y Thomas __________ que el tour es interesante. (decir)
3. Elena no __________ ir a las montañas. (querer)
4. Yo ya __________ la cuenta. (pagar)
5. ¿No __________ usted bien anoche? (dormir)
6. El policía me __________ el pasaporte. (pedir)
7. Yo __________ a los niños. (buscar)
8. Yo __________ a trabajar la semana pasada. (empezar)
9. Los García __________ una noticia en el periódico. (leer)
10. Nosotros __________ una botella de vino. (pedir)
11. Thomas no __________ terminar la comida. (poder)
12. ¿Cómo __________ tú la dirección de ella? (saber)
13. Nosotros __________ una hora libre. (tener)

Irregular Verbs in the Preterite

Complete the sentence with the correct form of the verb in the preterite.

1. Mamá me [di; dio] diez mil pesos.
2. Nosotros no [dijimos; dijisteis] nada.
3. ¿Qué [hice; hiciste] tú anoche?
4. ¿Dónde [puso; puse] el botones mi maleta?
5. Ełena [supiste; supo] dónde hay un buen mercado.
6. Thomas [estuve; estuvo] en su oficina toda la tarde.
7. Yo no [pude; puse] encontrar la oficina de correos.

Chapter 17

SOME USES OF *PARA*

Para is used to express the following:

to, in order to—*Trabajo para ganar plata.*

destined for, to be given to—*El libro es para ti.*

for (by a specific time)—*Estudien esta lección para mañana.*

for, in the direction of, toward—*Salimos para Acapulco.*

to be used for/by—*Es un hotel para turistas.*

for (compared with others)—*Para mí, el español es fácil.*

for (in the employ of)—*Trabajo para la universidad.*

Don't confuse the third person singular form of the verb *para* ('he/she stops,' 'you stop') with the preposition *para*. The context should tell you which part of speech and which meaning is most logical.

SOME USES OF *POR*

Por is used to express the following:

by, by means of	*por tren, por avión, por teléfono*
through, along	*por la playa o por el parque*
during, in (time period)	*por la mañana, por la tarde*
because of, due to	*estoy nerviosa por el examen*
for, in exchange for	*Te doy $20 por el libro.*
for the sake of	*Lo hago por la familia.*
for, in order to get	*Voy por café.*
for (for a period of time)	*Estaré aquí por dos horas.*

In idiomatic expressions:

por Dios	for Heaven's sake	*por lo general*	in general
por ejemplo	for example	*por lo menos*	at least
por eso	that's why	*por si acaso*	just in case
por favor	please	*por primera/*	for the first/
por fin	finally	*última vez*	last time

POSSESSIVE ADJECTIVES

The most common way to express possession in Spanish is with what are referred to as the unstressed possessive adjectives:

SINGULAR	PLURAL
mi, mis- my	*nuestro/a/os/as*- our
tu, tus- your, informal	*uestro/a/os/as*- your, informal [Spain]
su, sus- your, formal	*su, sus*- your
su, sus- his, her, its	*su, sus*- their

The possessive adjective preceeds the noun to which it refers. The ending of the adjective reflects the number of the thing possessed: *mi casa*, *mis libros*, *nuestra casa*, *nuestros libros*, *su casa*, *sus libros*, etc.

Nuestro and *vuestro* reflect gender (masculine or feminine) as well as number: *nuestras amigas*, *vuestros amigos*, etc.

Since *su* and *sus* can have multiple meanings ('your,' formal, singular and plural; 'his'; 'her'; 'its'; 'their,' masculine or feminine), another structure is sometimes used instead for clarification: definite article + noun + de + possessor.

su libro = el libro de...

usted
él
ella
Juan
ustedes
ellos
ellas
Juan y María

EXERCISES

Para and Por

Complete each sentence using *para* or *por*.

1. Caminamos [por; para] la playa todas las mañanas.
2. Este dinero es [por; para] usted.
3. Los Smith salieron [para; por] Acapulco.
4. Trabajo [por; para] una firma francesa.
5. Thomas vino [por; para] trabajar con nosotros.
6. Compré ropa [por; para] los niños.
7. Vuelva mañana [por; para] la mañana.

Possessive Adjectives

Draw a line to the correct possessive adjective.

1.	el carro (Uds.)	mi
2.	el dinero (yo)	sus
3.	las casas (Ud.)	mis
4.	los clientes (yo)	nuestro
5.	la dirección (tú)	su
6.	el número de teléfono (ella)	tu
7.	la esposa (él)	nuestras
8.	las amigas (nosotros)	su
9.	el hotel (nosotras)	su

Chapter 18

THE IMPERFECT TENSE

You have already learned one past tense in Spanish; the preterite, which is used to talk about actions or events that have been completed. The imperfect is another past tense in Spanish. It is used to talk about actions or events that were in progress in the past, things that were habitual or customary, or that happened over a long period of time. It is also used to describe ongoing mental, physical, or emotional states in the past, and to tell time in the past.

-ar verbs	-er verbs	-ir verbs
HABLAR	COMER	VIVIR
hablaba	comía	vivía
hablabas	comías	vivías
hablaba	comía	vivía
hablábamos	comíamos	vivíamos
hablabais	comíais	vivíais
hablaban	comían	vivían

Only three verbs are irregular in the imperfect tense.

IR	SER	VER
iba	era	veía
ibas	eras	veías
iba	era	veía
íbamos	éramos	veíamos
ibais	erais	veíais
iban	eran	veían

There are no stem-changes in the imperfect tense. Verbs that are stem-changing in the present or preterite are conjugated like regular verbs in the imperfect: *volvía*, *jugaba*, *pensaba*, *perdía*, etc.

VERBS LIKE *GUSTAR*

Remember the way that *gustar* is used? (See *Chapter 4* for a review of how to use *gustar*, if necessary.) Several other common verbs in Spanish follow the same pattern:

doler (ue)- to hurt	*importar*- to be important
encantar- to like a lot	*interesar*- to be of interest
faltar- to be lacking	*molestar*- to bother, annoy
fascinar- to fascinate	*parecer*- to seem, appear
fastidiar- to upset, bother	*preocupar*- to worry (someone)
hacer falta- to be lacking	*quedar*- to remain, be left

(*A mí*) *Me molestan los embotellamientos de tráfico.*
Traffic jams bother me.

(*A ti*) *¿Te interesan estos libros?*
Do these books interest you?

(*A usted*) *Le fascinan las representaciones folklóricas.*
The folkloric shows fascinate you.

(*A Elena*) *Le encanta el pescado.*
She likes fish a lot.

(*A nosotras*) *No nos queda mucho tiempo.*
We don't have much time left.

(*A vosotros*) *¿Os preocupa la idea?*
Does the idea worry you?

(*A ustedes*) *Les faltan 30,000 pesos.*
They lack 30,000 pesos.

(*A ellas*) *Les duele la cabeza.*
They have headaces.

EXERCISES

The Imperfect Tense

Fill in the blank with the correct form of the verb in the imperfect tense.

1. __________ buen tiempo cuando salimos de excursión. (hacer)
2. Thomas y Alberto siempre __________ de negocios. (hablar)
3. Yo __________ en Madrid cuando conocí a tu padre. (vivir)
4. Ellos __________ muy cansados cuando llegaron a Acapulco. (estar)
5. Nosotros __________ todos los días en ese restaurante. (comer)
6. Tú siempre __________ del trabajo a las seis. (salir)
7. Yo ________ a Cancún todos los años. (ir)
8. Las esposa de Roberto ________ su secretaria. (ser)
9. Nosotros __________ a las montañas con frecuencia. (ir)
10. Los padres de Eduardo __________ muy ricos. (ser)
11. Yo no __________ ver muy bien. (poder)
12. ¿Siempre __________ ustedes en autobús? (viajar)
13. No me __________ la ciudad donde vivía antes. (gustar)
14. Elena __________ visitar las tiendas. (querer)

Verbs like Gustar

Choose the correct form of the verb to complete the sentence.

1. Me [encanta; encantan] los camarones.
2. A Elena le [fastidian; fastidia] los viajes organizados.
3. ¿Te [duele; duelen] las piernas?
4. Nos [falta; faltan] treinta mil pesos.
5. A Karen le [preocupa; preocupan] la salud de Mario.
6. A los niños no les [interesa; interesan] una representación folklórica.
7. No nos [queda; quedan] muchos días libres.

Chapter 19

DEMONSTRATIVE ADJECTIVES AND PRONOUNS

this/these	that/those (nearby)	that/those (over there)
este estos	ese esos	aquel aquellos
esta estas	esa esas	aquella aquellas

When used as adjectives, the demonstratives precede the noun and must agree in number and gender with the noun they describe: *este hotel*, *esa comida*, *aquellos hombres*, etc.

When used as a pronoun ('this one,' 'that one,' 'these,' 'those,' etc.), the demonstratives have accent marks: *este libro y ése* ('this book and that one'); *esta puerta y ésa* ('this door and that one'), etc.

The difference between *ese* and *aquel* is one of relative distance. The thing farthest away from the speaker is *aquel*, whereas *ese* implies that it is a bit closer.

COMPARISONS OF INEQUALITY

When you are comparing things that are not equal ('more than'; 'less than,' 'better than,' etc.), use these formulas:

más + adjective/adverb/noun + *que* = more than
menos + adjective/adverb/noun + *que* = less than

Roberto es más inteligente que Pablo.
Roberto is more intelligent than Pablo.

Pablo es menos inteligente que Roberto.
Pablo is less intelligent than Roberto.

Roberto habla más rápido que Pablo.
Roberto speaks more quickly than Pablo.

Pablo habla menos rápido que Roberto.
Pablo speaks less rapidly than Roberto.

Roberto tiene más amigos que Pablo.
Roberto has more friends than Pablo.

Pablo tiene menos amigos que Roberto.
Pablo has less (fewer) friends than Roberto.

Some comparison forms are irregular and must be memorized.

bueno/bien	*mejor*- better
malo/mal	*peor*- worse
joven	*menor*- younger
viejo	*mayor*- older

EXERCISES

Demonstrative Adjectives

Choose the correct demonstrative adjective or pronoun.

1. [esta; este] casa
2. [esas; esos] hoteles
3. [aquel; aquellos] hombres
4. [aquella; aquel] mujer
5. [este; esta] noche
6. [esa; esas] medicina
7. [esta; este] mañana
8. [aquella; aquel] pantalón
9. [esa; esas] camisas
10. [este; esta] viaje
11. [aquellos; aquel] autobuses
12. [esos; esas] montañas

Comparisons of Inequality

Fill in the blank with the correct comparative adjective.

1. Estos libros son ____________ que ésos. (interesante)
2. La comida en este restaurante es ____________ que la comida en el hotel. (bueno)
3. Thomas es ____________ que Elena. (viejo)
4. Este pañuelo es ____________ que ése. (elegante)
5. Silvia es ____________ que Elena. (joven)
6. Tú hablas inglés ____________ que yo. (bien)
7. Ahora me siento ____________ que antes. (mal)
8. Aquellos libros eran ____________ que éstos. (barato)

Chapter 20

THE MEANING OF HAY

Hay is an irregular form of the the verb *haber*. It means 'there is' or 'there are,' and it is used to point out the existence or presence of someone or something:

Hay un restaurante bueno cerca de aquí.
There is a good restaurant close to here.

Hay muchos taxis en la calle.
There are many taxis in the street.

Hay cinco socios en la firma.
There are five partners in the firm.

Hay diez empleados en la oficina.
There are ten employees in the office.

When referring to the past, the verb form becomes *había* (imperfect) or sometimes *hubo*:

Había (Hubo) un restaurante bueno cerca de aquí.
There was a good restaurant close to here.

Había (Hubo) muchos taxis en la calle.
There were many taxis in the street.

Había (Hubo) cinco socios en la firma.
There were five partners in the firm.

Había (Hubo) diez empleados en la oficina.
There were ten employees in the office.

Note: Remember, *hay*, *había*, and *hubo* point out the existence or presence of something. If you are pointing out the location of specific persons or things, use a form of *estar*:

Roberto está en casa.

Roberto is at home.

Silvia y Elena están en el mercado.

Silvia and Elena are at the market.

La carta está en la mesa.

The letter is on the table.

Los libros están en el suelo.

The books are on the floor.

SOME USES OF *LO*

The word *lo* can be a direct object pronoun; 'him,' 'it,' 'you' (which you will study in *Chapter 21*), but it can also function as a neuter article to describe an abstract idea. In English, this structure is usually expressed by 'the...thing'. *Lo más importante es que ustedes lleguen a tiempo* ('The most important thing is that you all arrive on time'). *Lo malo es que Thomas no puede encontrar una casa amueblada* ('The bad thing is that Thomas can't find a furnished house').

Lo can also refer to a whole situation: *déjelo* ('forget the whole thing'). *No lo comprendo* ('I don't understand anything').

EXERCISES

The Meaning of Hay

Choose the correct verb to complete the sentence.

1. No [es; hay; está] nadie aquí que pueda contestar.
2. [Era; Había; Estaban] mucha gente en la calle.
3. Thomas y Elena [eran; estaban; había] en Acapulco.
4. Thomas [está; es; hay] un hombre de negocios.
5. Los niños [están; son; hay] en casa.
6. [Son; Hay; Están] dos fiestas esta noche.
7. ¿[Es; Está; Hay] un banco cerca de aquí?
8. Karen [está; hay; es] en el mercado.

Uses of Lo

Draw a line to the correct translation.

1.	lo importante	Say it.
2.	no lo comprendo	Leave it.
3.	lo mejor	the most interesting thing
4.	lo más interesante	the important thing
5.	no lo sé	I don't understand it.
6.	dígalo	I don't know.
7.	déjelo	the best thing

Chapter 21

DIRECT OBJECT PRONOUNS

The direct object of a sentence answers the question 'what?' or 'whom?': 'What do you want to see?' ('The city'); 'Whom do you see on the balcony?' ('My wife'). To replace the direct object noun with a pronoun, you must choose the correct direct object pronoun, the one that reflects the number and gender of the noun it replaces:

me (me)	*nos* (us)
te (you, informal)	*os* (you all, informal)
lo, la (you, formal)	*los, las* (you, formal)
lo, la (him, her, it)	*los, las* (them)

Notice that the direct object pronouns, like the indirect object pronouns, immediately precede the conjugated verb: (*¿A mí*?) *Si, ellos me conocen.* (*¿A Elena*?) *Yo no la conozco.* (*¿El dinero*?) *Lo tengo aquí.* (*¿Las maletas*?) *No las veo.*

The pronoun can instead be attached to an infinitive: *Lo voy a ver* or *Voy a verlo. Te quiero ayudar* or *Quiero ayudarte.*

PLACEMENT OF OBJECT PRONOUNS

As you have seen, both direct and indirect object pronouns immediately precede a conjugated verb: *Thomas le pide el número*; *Ahora mismo le doy el regalo*; *Roberto me recibe y me hace pasar*; *Yo te indico dónde está la oficina*; *No lo conocemos.*

These pronoun forms can also be attached to an infinitive: *¿Puede decirme dónde están los servicios*?; *Podemos hacerle un precio especial*; *¿Vas a llamarme*? They can also be attached to gerunds: *Estoy comprándoles los libros*; *Estamos buscándolo.*

With an affirmative command, the pronoun is also attached to the end of the verb: (*¿Las maletas*?) *Póngalas aquí*; *Déjelo*; *Dígale lo que le pasa*; *Tráigame una cerveza.*

With a negative command, the pronoun precedes the verb: *No las ponga allí*; *No me diga.*

SOME USES OF *SE*

You have seen *Se* used as a reflexive pronoun in Spanish, but it also has some other uses:

1. As the impersonal subject 'you,' 'one,' 'people': *Se come bien en este restaurante* ('One eats well in this restaurant'); *¿Cómo se dice 'today' en español*? ('How does one say today in Spanish?'); *Nunca se sabe* ('One never knows'). Notice that in this construction, the verb is always in the third person singular.
2. In passive constructions: *Aquí se habla español* ('Spanish is spoken here'); *Se venden libros* ('Books are sold'). Notice that in these constructions the verb may be in the third person singular or plural, depending on whether the thing you're referring to (the grammatical subject) is singular or plural.

Note that the formal command of *dar*; *dé*, loses the accent mark when a single pronoun is added to form the affirmative command: *Deme el libro* ('Give me the book').

EXERCISE

Direct Object Pronouns

Replace the direct object in each sentence with a direct object pronoun.

Example: No puedo ver a tu marido. > No puedo verlo.

1. Tengo el dinero aquí.

   ____

2. Yo no conzoco a Elena.

   ____

3. Ella llama a ti.

   ____

4. Nosotros compramos los libros.

   ____

5. Ellos dan el regalo a mi.

   ____

6. Mario visita las tiendas.

   ____

7. Karen escribe a nosotros.

   ____

Chapter 22

SEQUENCE OF OBJECT PRONOUNS

When both a direct and indirect object pronoun appear in a sentence, the indirect object pronoun will precede the direct object pronoun: *Me lo dice*; *Te la mando ahora.* When both the direct and indirect object pronouns are in the third person, the indirect object pronoun must be replaced by *se*:

le/les and lo/la/los/las — se lo/se la/se los/se las

¿Le das los libros a Silvia?

Are you giving the books to Silvia?

Sí, se los doy.

Yes, I'm giving them to her.

¿Les compras los juguetes?

Are you buying the toys for them?

Sí, se los compro.

Yes, I'm buying them for them.

¿Me trae un café?

Will you bring me a coffee?

Sí, se lo traigo ahora.

Yes, I'll bring it to you [formal] now.

Note that when object pronouns are attached to affirmative commands, gerunds, or infinitives, you may need to add an accent mark to preserve the stress of the word: *Búscalo*; *Estoy buscándolo*; *Tráigamelo*; *Voy a traérselo*; but *Voy a traerlo*.

SUBJUNCTIVE AFTER IMPERSONAL EXPRESSIONS

After impersonal expressions that indicate a willing, wish, command, preference, desire, necessity, opinion, etc. on the part of the speaker that another person do (or not do) something, the subjunctive is used in the dependent clause, after the word *que*:

Es importante que usted hable con la directora.

It's important that you speak with the director.

Es necesario que Elena tome un taxi.

It's necessary that Elena take a taxi.

¡Es terrible que no sepas hablar español!

It's terrible that you don't know how to speak Spanish!

Es posible que sea el efecto de la comida.

It's possible that it is the effect of the food.

No es preciso que usted tome medicina especial.

It's not necessary for you to take special medicine.

However, if the expression does not reflect the desire to influence a specific person to do something, but instead is a statement that people in general should do something, then the infinitive (*-ar*, *-er*, *-ir* forms), and not the subjunctive, is used.

Es necesario evitar el alcohol.

It's necessary to avoid alchohol.

Es preferible ir en autobús.

It's preferable to go by bus.

Es posible comprar comida aquí.

It's possible to buy food here.

THE SUBJUNCTIVE IN ADVERBIAL CLAUSES

If an action has not yet occurred, a native speaker of Spanish will use the subjunctive after certain adverbial clauses such as: *tan pronto como* ('as soon as'), *cuando* ('when'), *después de que* ('after'), *en cuanto* ('as soon as'), *hasta que* ('until'), and *mientras* ('while,' 'as long as').

Podemos hablar del tema cuando usted llegue (you haven't arrived yet).

Puedo quedarme en un hotel mientras esté en México (for however long I am in Mexico — I haven't left yet).
Elena viene tan pronto como yo encuentre un apartamento (I haven't found an apartment yet).

If the action has already taken place and there is therefore no doubt about its outcome, the subjunctive is not used: *Cuando estuve en Acapulco, fui a la playa* (I went to Acapulco in the past).

EXERCISES

Subjunctive After Impersonal Expressions

Fill in the blank with the correct form of the subjunctive.

1. Es importante que usted __________ las comidas pesadas. (evitar)
2. ¿Es necesario que yo __________ alguna medicina especial? (tomar)
3. Es preciso que nosotros __________ al mercado hoy. (ir)
4. Es preferible que ustedes __________ conmigo al mercado. (venir)
5. ¡Es increíble que tú __________ tanto! (comprar)
6. ¡Es terrible que ellos no __________ acompañarnos! (poder)
7. Es posible que ellos no __________ pescado hoy. (tener)

The Subjunctive in Adverbial Clauses

Complete the sentence with the correct form of the subjunctive or indicative.

1. Iremos a España cuando nosotros [terminemos; terminamos] el trabajo aquí.
2. Te llamaré tan pronto como [llego; llegue] al hotel.
3. No te olvides de comprar la carne cuando [estés; estás] en el mercado.
4. En cuanto Thomas [encuentra; encuentre] un apartamento, va a traer a su familia.
5. Siempre compro regalos cuando yo [esté; estoy] en Acapulco.
6. Elena no quiere manejar mientras ella [esté; está] en México.
7. Usted no puede marcharse hasta que [consigue; consiga] un pasaporte.
8. Cuando [vaya; voy] de vacaciones, me gusta viajar en autobús.
9. Karen siempre le llama a Mario tan pronto como [llega; llegue] al hotel.

Chapter 23

INFORMAL *TU* COMMANDS

Affirmative *tú* commands have the same form as the third person singular (*él*, *ella*, *usted*) of the present indicative: *Habla* (*tú*); *Cierra* (*tú*) *la ventana; Limpia (tú) los dormitorios*; *Come (tú) las verduras*; *Trae (tú) los regalos*; *Corre (tú) en el parque*.

Negative *tú* commands have the same form as the *tú* form of the present subjunctive: *No hables (tú)*; *No cierres (tú) la ventana*; *No limpies (tú) los dormitorios*; *No comas (tú) los chocolates*; *No traigas (tú) los regalos*; *No corras (tú) en el parque*.

As with usted commands, direct, indirect and reflexive pronouns are attached to affirmative commands: *tráeme*, *explícame*, *déjalo*, *levántate*, *siéntate*, etc.

Direct, indirect, and reflexive pronouns precede a negative *tú* command: *no me traigas*, *no me expliques*, *no lo dejes*, *no te levantes*, *no te sientes*, etc.

IRREGULAR *TU* COMMANDS

There are only a few irregular *tú* commands, and these are irregular only in the affirmative command form. The negative command forms are the same as the *tú* form of the present subjunctive.

decir: di, no digas

hacer: haz, no hagas

ir: ve, no vayas

poner: pon, no pongas

salir: sal, no salgas

ser: sé, no seas

tener: ten, no tengas

venir: ven, no vengas

EXERCISE

Irregular *tú* Commands

Fill in the blank with the correct *tú* command.

1. ____________ la comida. (preparar)
2. ____________ las verduras. (comprar)
3. ____________ todo. (hacerlo)
4. ____________ a la lavandería. (ir)
5. ____________ conmigo. (venir)
6. ____________ paciencia. (tener)
7. ____________ el vino en la mesa. (poner)
8. ____________ temprano. (salir)
9. ____________ la mesa. (recoger)

Chapter 24

PRETERITE VS. IMPERFECT

The preterite is used to narrate completed actions in the past. Certain words like *ayer* ('yesterday'), *anoche* ('last night'), *el año pasado* ('last year'), and *la semana pasada* ('last week'), are associated with the preterite since they usually refer to specific events that are now completed.

The imperfect is used to narrate actions that were habitual or ongoing in the past. There is no reference to whether or not these things were ever completed, or whether they continue into the present time. Phrases like *siempre* ('always'), *frecuentemente* ('frequently'), and *todos los días* ('daily'), are often associated with the imperfect. The difference between the preterite and imperfect is often very subtle, and even native speakers will occasionally disagree about which form is correct. You should study examples and try to imitate native speakers when possible.

COMPARISONS OF EQUALITY

To compare nouns, adjectives, or adverbs that are equal ('as ... as'; 'as much/many ... as') use these formulas:

tan + adjective or adverb + *como*

Eduardo es tan inteligente como Roberto.

Eduardo is as intelligent as Roberto.

Eduardo habla tan rápido como Roberto.

Eduardo speaks as quickly as Roberto.

tanto/a/os/as + noun + *como*

Tengo tanto dinero como tú.

I have as much money as you.

Bebo tanta cerveza como tú.

I drink as much beer as you.

Ella tiene tantos amigos como yo.

She has as many friends as I.

Ella tiene tantas amigas como yo.

She has as many friends (f.) as I.

Notice that *tanto* will agree in number and gender with the noun it describes: *tantas horas*, *tantos días*, etc.

EXERCISES

Preterite vs. Imperfect

Choose the correct preterite or imperfect form of the verb.

1. El sábado pasado, yo [estaba; estuve] en Mérida cuando llegó mi amigo.
2. Nosotros [fuimos; íbamos] todos los días a la playa.
3. Ayer yo [vi; veía] a Elena en el mercado.
4. Mi marido siempre me [llamó; llamaba] a las cuatro de la tarde.
5. Yo [conocí; conocía] a Eduardo en una fiesta.
6. Ayer yo [recibí; recibía] seis llamadas telefónicas.
7. ¿Les [gustó; gustaba] la representación folklórica?

Comparisons of Equality

Fill in the blank with the correct comparitive form.

1. Mario tiene _____________ hijos como Thomas.
2. Elena es _____________ alta como Thomas.
3. Thomas maneja _____________ rápido como yo.
4. Tú tienes _____________ camisas como él.
5. Ese vestido es _____________ elegante como éste.
6. Mis trajes son _____________ viejos como los tuyos.
7. Thomas tiene _____________ trajes como yo.
8. Karen tiene _____________ blusas como Elena.
9. Silvia no necesita comprar _____________ comida como Karen.

Chapter 25

THE PAST PARTICIPLE

The past participle is formed in Spanish by adding *-ado* to the stem of regular *-ar* verbs, and *-ido* to the stem of regular *-er* or *-ir* verbs: *hablar* > *hablado*; *poder* > *podido*; *vivir* > *vivido*, etc.

The past participle can often be used as an adjective (usually with the verb *estar*). Then, it has four forms, reflecting the number and gender of the noun it describes:

El precio está confirmado.	The price is confirmed.
La tarifa está confirmada.	The fare is confirmed.
Los fondos están confirmados.	The funds are confirmed.
Las reservaciones están confirmadas.	The reservations are confirmed.

The past participle can also be used with the verb *ser* to construct the passive voice: *La comida fue preparada por mamá* ('The food was prepared by Mom'). Again, the past participle reflects number and gender of the noun it describes. The passive construction with *ser* + past participle is not as common in Spanish as it is in English. The active voice should be used whenever possible: *Mamá preparó la comida* ('Mom made the food').

IRREGULAR PAST PARTICIPLES

The following verbs have irregular past participles which must be memorized.

Abrir	abierto	Morir	muerto
Decir	dicho	Poner	puesto
Cubrir	cubierto	Resolver	resuelto
Descubrir	descubierto	Romper	roto
Escribir	escrito	Ver	visto
Hacer	hecho	Volver	vuelto

An accent mark is added to the past participle of *-er* and *-ir* verbs with stems ending in a vowel: *caer* > *caído*, *creer* > *creído*, *leer* > *leído*, *oír* > *oído*, *traer* > *traído*, etc.

THE PRESENT PERFECT TENSE

The present perfect is constructed by using a conjugated form of the irregular verb *haber* with the past participle.

he comido	hemos comido
has comido	habéis comido
ha comido	han comido

The past participle does not change form when it is used in the present perfect tense. For example, *Ella ha comido*, *nosotros hemos comido*, *ustedes han comido*, etc. Like its English counterpart, the present perfect tense is used to refer to the past. In the affirmative, it refers to an action that has already taken place; *Elena ha llegado* ('Elena has arrived'). In the negative, it refers to something that has not happened yet; *No ha llegado* ('She hasn't arrived yet').

EXERCISES

The Past Participle

Fill in the blank with the correct past participle.

1. ¿Ha __________ una transferencia desde los Estados Unidos? (llegar)
2. He __________ una cuenta en el banco. (abrir)
3. Karen ha __________ que quiere cheques de viaje. (decir)
4. Elena ha __________ un depósito. (hacer)
5. El libro fue __________ por mi profesor. (escribir)
6. Los niños han __________ la ventana. (romper)
7. ¿Has __________ a Mario hoy? (ver)
8. Silvia todavía no ha __________ de la reunión. (volver)
9. Eduardo me ha __________ por teléfono. (llamar)

Irregular Past Participles

Choose the correct irregular past participle.

1. Roberto me ha [hecho; dicho] que usted va a trabajar con nosotros.
2. Los padres de Thomas le han [escrito; resuelto] una carta.
3. Lupe, ¿has [hecho; puesto] las camas hoy?
4. Los Smith han [visto; vuelto] de vacaciones hoy.
5. ¿Por qué no has [dicho; abierto] la puerta?
6. Nosotros no hemos [visto; muerto] todavía esa representación.
7. Elena y yo hemos [descubierto; roto] una tienda maravillosa.

The Present Perfect Tense

Complete the sentence with the correct conjugated form of *haber* to form the present perfect tense.

1. El dinero no _____________ llegado todavía al banco.
2. Thomas _____________ abierto una cuenta de ahorros.
3. Elena y Silvia no _____________ vuelto del mercado.
4. ¿Qué _____________ hecho tú?
5. Ustedes _____________ depositado cinco millones de pesos.
6. Nosotros _____________ recibido una transferencia desde Chicago.
7. Yo no _____________ visto a Thomas.

Chapter 26

SOME STEM CHANGES AND SPELLING CHANGES IN THE PRESENT SUBJUNCTIVE

In the present subjunctive, the *-ar* and *-er* stem-changing verbs have the same pattern of stem changes as in the present indicative, only the endings are different.

PENSAR	VOLVER	DORMIR	PREFERIR
(ie)	(ue)	(ue, u)	(ie, i)
piense	vuelva	duerma	prefiera
pienses	vuelvas	duermas	prefieras
piense	vuelva	duerma	prefiera
pensemos	volvamos	durmamos	prefiramos
penséis	volváis	durmáis	prefiráis
piensen	vuelvan	duerman	prefieran

-Ir stem-changing verbs have a slightly different pattern in the subjunctive than in the present indicative. Recall that these are the same verbs that have a different stem change in the preterite, in the third person form. The same stem change seen in the preterite is seen in the subjunctive in the *nosotros/as* and *vosotros/as* forms.

As you have already seen, verbs ending in *-car*, *-gar*, and *-zar* have a spelling change in all forms of the present subjunctive, with *c* > *qu*, *g* > *gu*, and *z* > *c*.

BUSCAR	PAGAR	EMPEZAR
busque	pague	empiece
busques	pagues	empieces
busque	pague	empiece
busquemos	paguemos	empecemos
busquéis	paguéis	empecéis
busquen	paguen	empiecen

SUBJUNCTIVE AFTER VERBS OF WILLING

One of the most common uses of the subjunctive is after verbs of willing, such as *querer* ('to want'), *desear* ('to want'), *insistir en* ('to insist on'), *mandar* ('to order'), *preferir* ('to prefer'), *prohibir* ('to prohibit'), *recomendar* ('to recommend'), *decir* ('to tell' someone to do something), *pedir* ('to ask' someone to do something), and *permitir* ('to permit). Notice that in the examples of the use of the subjunctive with the verbs of willing in the settings and dialogues, there is one person speaking who wants another person to do something. That is, there must be a change of subject in order to use the subjunctive—one subject wants to influence the other subject to do something. *Thomas quiere que la operadora llame...*; *Thomas quiere que la secretaria le indique...*; *Thomas quiere que el camarero le traiga...*, etc. The subjunctive is used after the conjunction *que* in the subordinate clause of the sentence. If there is no change of subject, the subjunctive is not used: *Thomas quiere comer*; *Thomas quiere llamar*; *Thomas quiere encontrar...*; etc.

EXERCISES

Stem and Spelling Changes in the Present Subjunctive

Fill in the blank with the correct subjunctive form of the verb.

1. Thomas quiere que el camarero le __________ agua. (traer)
2. El médico me dice que yo __________ esta pastilla. (tomar)
3. Es preferible que ustedes __________ con un tour organizado. (ir)
4. Elena insiste en que Lupe __________ todo el trabajo hoy. (hacer)
5. Recomiendo que tú __________ un buen mecánico. (buscar)
6. ¡Es terrible que nosotros no __________ ni un momento libre esta semana! (tener)
7. ¡Es ridículo que ustedes no __________ tarjetas de crédito! (aceptar)
8. Quiero que tú me __________ algo. (explicar)

Subjunctive After Verbs of Willing

Choose the correct form of the verb.

1. Elena quiere que el mecánico [revisa; revise; revisar] el aceite.
2. El mecánico no quiere que yo [paga; pague; pagar] con tarjeta de crédito.
3. Roberto prohibe que sus hijos [manejar; manejen; manejan] el carro nuevo.
4. Karen pide que el mecánico le [ponga; pone; poner] agua en la batería.
5. Thomas insiste en que Elena [vuelve; vuelva; volver] a casa ahora mismo.
6. El médico me recomienda que yo [duerma; duerme; dormir] un mínimo de siete horas cada noche.
7. Los Smith quieren [encuentre; encontrar; encuentra] una casa en el centro.
8. Silvia quiere [comprar; compre; compra] unas salchichas.

Chapter 27

SOME USES OF *HACE*

The verb form *hace* is used in many weather expressions. These are idioms and should be memorized.

¿Qué tiempo hace?	What's the weather like?
Hace buen tiempo.	The weather is nice.
Hace mal tiempo.	The weather is bad.
Hace frío.	It's cold.
Hace calor.	It's hot.
Hace viento.	It's windy.
Hace sol.	It's sunny.
Hace fresco.	It's cool.

When used with a time expression and a verb in the present tense, (*desde*) *hace* means for a certain amount of time: *(Desde) Hace un mes estoy en México* ('I have been in Mexico for a month'). When used with the past tense, it means 'ago': *Lo conocí hace seis años* ('I met him six years ago').

HOLIDAYS AND SPECIAL OCCASIONS

la Semana Santa	Holy Week
la Pascua (Florida)	Easter
el Día de Independencia	Independence Day
el Día de los Muertos	All Soul's Day
la Nochebuena	Christmas Eve
la Navidad	Christmas
la Noche Vieja	New Year's Eve
el Día de Año Nuevo	New Year's Day
el aniversario	anniversary
el cumpleaños	birthday
los días festivos/las fiestas	holidays
las vacaciones	vacation
¡felicitaciones!	congratulations

DATES, SEASONS, MONTHS OF THE YEAR

La fecha	The date
¿Cuál es la fecha de hoy?	What is today's date?
(Hoy) Es el primero de abril.	Today is April 1.
(Hoy) Es el cinco de marzo.	Today is March 5.

Note: The ordinal number *primero* is used to express the first day of the month, but cardinal numbers (*dos*, *tres*, etc.) are used for the other days.

Los meses del año ('the months of the year'):

enero	January
febrero	February
marzo	March
abril	April
mayo	May
junio	June
julio	July
agosto	August
se(p)tiembre	September
octubre	October
noviembre	November
diciembre	December

Note: The months are not capitalized in Spanish.

Las estaciones del año ('the seasons of the year'):

el invierno	winter
la primavera	spring
el verano	summer
el otoño	fall

EXERCISE

Holidays, Seasons, and Months

Circle the word that does not belong.

1. ¿Cuál es diferente? [la Noche Vieja; La Nochebuena; el verano; La Navidad]
2. ¿Cuál es diferente? [marzo; otoño; febrero; enero]
3. ¿Cuál es diferente? [octubre; primavera; verano; invierno]
4. ¿Cuál es diferente? [el cumpleaños; viento; felicitaciones; las fiestas]
5. ¿Cuál es diferente? [sol; noviembre; calor; buen tiempo]
6. ¿Cuál es diferente? [la Pascua; diciembre; la Semana Santa; la primavera]

Chapter 28

SOME VERBS THAT REQUIRE PREPOSITIONS

1. These verbs are followed by the preposition *a*.

   aprender a (to learn to)
   ayudar a (to help)
   comenzar a (to begin to)
   empezar a (to begin to)
   enseñar a (to teach to)
   invitar a (to invite to)
   ir a (to go to)
   volver a (to return to)

2. These verbs are followed by *de*.

   acabar de (to just finish)
   acordarse de (to remember)
   dejar de (to stop)
   olvidarse de (to forget)
   tener ganas de (to feel like)
   tratar de (to try to)

3. *Insistir* ('to insist') is followed by *en*, and will call for the subjunctive in the subordinate clause if there is a change of subject.
4. *Pensar* ('to think') can be followed by *en* or *de*, depending on the meaning intended: *Pienso en ti* ('I'm thinking about you' ['You're on my mind']). *¿Qué piensas de ella*? ('What do you think about her?' ['What is your reaction,' 'your feeling about her?']).

Note: The prepositions are used only when the grammatical object follows the verb. If no object follows, then no preposition is used: *¿Me ayudas a limpiar las ventanas*? *Sí, te ayudo*.

THE CONDITIONAL TENSE

Like the future tense, the conditional is formed by adding endings (*-ía*, *-ías*, *-ía*, *-íamos*, *-íais*, *-ían*) to the entire infinitive. Do not confuse the conditional forms of *-er* and *-ir* verbs with the imperfect. The endings for the latter are added to the stem, not to the infinitive.

HABLAR

hablaría, hablarías, hablaría, hablaríamos, hablaríais, hablarían

COMER

comería, comerías, comería, comeríamos, comeríais, comerían

VIVIR

viviría, vivirías, viviría, viviríamos, viviríais, vivirían

The conditional is used to talk about things that would happen under certain circumstances: *Un permanente le quedaría bien* ('A permanent would look good on you'), or to make polite requests; *Me gustaría [pedir] el pescado* ('I would like [to order] the fish').

SOME IRREGULAR VERBS IN THE CONDITIONAL TENSE

DECIR

diría, dirías, diría, diríamos, diríais, dirían

HABER

habría, habrías, habría, habríamos, habríais, habrían

HACER

haría, harías, haría, haríamos, haríais, harían

PODER

podría, podrías, podría, podríamos, podríais, podrían

QUERER

querría, querrías, querría, querríamos, querríais, querrían

SABER

sabría, sabrías, sabría, sabríamos, sabríais, sabrían

PONER

pondría, pondrías, pondría, pondríamos, pondríais, pondrían

SALIR

saldría, saldrías, saldría, saldríamos, saldríais, saldrían

TENER

tendría, tendrías, tendría, tendríamos, tendríais, tendrían

VENIR

vendría, vendrías, vendría, vendríamos, vendríais, vendrían

EXERCISES

The Conditional Tense

Choose the correct subject to complete the sentence.

1. [Thomas; Yo; Tú] dijo que hablaría con Elena.
2. [Nosotros; Ella; Ellos] comería en un restaurante mexicano.
3. [Tú; Thomas; Nosotros] viviríamos en México por un año.
4. [Ellos; Karen; Yo] dirían que Roberto es su amigo.
5. [Nosotros; Ellas; Tú] harían un buen almuerzo para ti.
6. [Karen y Mario; Yo; Tú] podría visitar Acapulco.
7. [Tú; Ellos; Mario] saldrías del trabajo a las seis.
8. [Nosotras; Karen; Ellos] tendría que reservar cuatro puestos.
9. [Mario; Los niños; Tú] vendría a Taxco con Karen.

Irregular Verbs in the Conditional Tense

Fill in the blank with the correct conditional form of the verb.

1. Por favor, ¿__________ usted decirme la hora? (poder)
2. Pensé que los padres de Thomas __________ para las fiestas de Navidad. (venir)
3. Yo __________ cambiar cien dólares, por favor. (querer)
4. El mecánico me dijo que él me __________ aire en la rueda. (poner)
5. ¿__________ usted tan amable de indicarme el camino? (ser)
6. La permanente le __________ más volumen. (dar)
7. Eso le __________ bien a mi marido. (venir)
8. A mi marido, no le __________ tantos rizos. (gustar)
9. ¿Qué __________ tú en mi lugar? (hacer)

Chapter 29

THE SUBJUNCTIVE AFTER VERBS OF EMOTION

The subjunctive is used after certain expressions of emotion, when the speaker shows emotion about the actions of another person, as in *Me alegro de que estés aquí* ('I'm glad that you're here'). The subjunctive is also used after impersonal expressions of emotion, as in *Es una lástima que no puedas acompañarnos* ('It's a pity that you can't come with us').

You should recognize these expressions as some that will require the use of the subjunctive in the subordinate clause, after the word *que*: *alegrarse* ('to be glad'), *esperar* ('to hope'), *sentir* ('to regret'), *temer* ('to be afraid'), *asombrarse* ('to be surprised'), *sorprenderse* ('to surprise'), *enfadarse* ('to be angry'), *enojarse* ('to be angry'), *es una lástima* ('it's a pity'), *es triste* ('it's sad'), *es escandaloso* ('it's scandalous'), *es terrible* ('it's terrible'), and so forth.

SUBJUNCTIVE IN EXPRESSIONS OF DOUBT

The subjunctive is used after expressions of doubt or uncertainty: *dudar* ('to doubt'), *no creer* ('not to believe'), *no estar seguro/a* ('not to be sure'), *no es verdad* ('it's not true'), *es dudoso* ('it's doubtful'), *no es cierto* ('it's uncertain'), etc. As always, the subjunctive will be used after the word *que* in the subordinate clause of the sentence: *Dudo que pueda llegar antes de las nueve*; *No creo que el viaje sea largo*; *Es dudoso que la casa esté amueblada*; *No es cierto que tengan pescado en el mercado*.

If there is no doubt or uncertainty in the mind of the speaker, then the indicative is used: *Es cierto que mis padres vienen para Navidad; No hay duda de que sus nietos quieren verlos*; *Creo que van a estar aquí dos semanas*.

Note: *Creo que* and *no dudo que* are expressions of certainty, and thus require the indicative in the subordinate clause. *No creo que* and dudo que are expressions of doubt that call for the subjunctive in the subordinate clause.

EXERCISES

The Subjunctive After Verbs of Emotion

Fill in the blank with the correct subjunctive form of the verb.

1. Me alegro de que usted __________ acompañarnos el viernes. (poder)
2. Es una lástima que a ustedes no les __________ el teatro. (gustar)
3. Me fastidia que ellos no __________ carne en este restaurante. (servir)
4. ¿Te sorprende que las entradas __________ tan caras? (ser)
5. ¡Me asombra que tú __________ a mis primos en Chicago! (conocer)
6. Siento que nosotros no __________ más tiempo libre para ver la ciudad. (tener)
7. Espero que nosotras ___________ el trabajo pronto. (terminar)

Subjunctive in Expressions of Doubt

Choose the correct subjunctive or indicative form.

1. Estoy segura que [quedan; queden] entradas.
2. Es dudoso que [hay; hayan] dos asientos juntos.
3. Dudo que él [puede; pueda] pasar por su hotel.
4. Thomas no cree que Roberto y Silvia [quieran; quieren] acompañarlos al teatro.
5. Es cierto que muchas personas [van; vayan] a las funciones en Bellas Artes.
6. Creo que los actores [sean; son] de Buenos Aires.
7. No es cierto que la directora [hable; habla] inglés.
8. Es verdad que mis padres [vengan; vienen] para las fiestas de Navidad.

Chapter 30

RECIPROCAL ACTIONS

The plural reflexive pronouns (*nos*, *os*, *se*) can be used to express mutual or reciprocal actions, generally expressed in English as 'each other'.

Roberto y Thomas se saludan ('They greet each other'). *Elena y Thomas se escriben* ('They write to each other'). *Ustedes se quieren mucho* ('You all love each other a lot'). *Ustedes se conocen, ¿verdad?* ('You all know each other, don't you?'). *Vosotros os veis con frecuencia* ('You all see each other often'). *Nosotros nos conocemos hace años* ('We've know each other for years').

SOME IRREGULAR VERBS IN THE FUTURE TENSE

DECIR

diré, dirás, dirá, diremos, diréis, dirán

HABER

habré, habrás, habrá, habremos, habréis, habrán

HACER

haré, harás, hará, haremos, haréis, harán

PODER

podré, podrás, podrá, podremos, podréis, podrán

QUERER

querré, querrás, querrá, querremos, querréis, querrán

SABER

sabré, sabrás, sabrá, sabremos, sabréis, sabrán

PONER

pondré, pondrás, pondrá, pondremos, pondréis, pondrán

SALIR

saldré, saldrás, saldrá, saldremos, saldréis, saldrán

TENER

tendré, tendrás, tendrá, tendremos, tendréis, tendrán

VENIR

vendré, vendrás, vendrá, vendremos, vendréis, vendrán

The irregular verbs for the future tense have the same forms as the irregular verbs for the conditional that you learned in *Chapter 28*, but they use the future endings: *-é*, *-ás*, *-á*, *-emos*, *-éis*, *-án*.

EXERCISES

Reciprocal Actions

Complete the sentence with the correct pronoun to express reciprocal action.

1. Thomas y Elena _____________ llaman frecuentemente por teléfono.
2. Nosotros casi nunca _____________ escribimos.
3. Eduardo y Thomas _____________ veían todos los días en la oficina.
4. Silvia y yo raramente _____________ hablamos.
5. ¿_____________ conocen ustedes?
6. Mi marido y yo _____________ queremos mucho.

Irregular Verbs in the Future Tense

Fill in the blank with the correct future form of the irregular verb.

1. Ustedes _____________ que terminar el trabajo mañana. (tener)
2. Nostros _____________ causar una buena impresión. (querer)
3. El vuelo _____________ a las tres y cuarto. (salir)
4. Yo _____________ el maletín debajo de mi asiento. (poner)
5. ¿_____________ la directora que no hemos terminado? (saber)
6. ¿Qué _____________ mi esposo cuando me vea con una permanente? (decir)
7. Ustedes _____________ llamarme desde el aeropuerto. (poder)
8. ¿_____________ Elena y los niños al aeropuerto con Thomas? (venir)
9. ¿_____________ tiempo suficiente para documentar el equipaje? (haber)
10. Thomas _____________ otro viaje al Ecuador en octubre. (hacer)

Exercise Answers

Chapter 1

Definite and Indefinite Articles

1. el señor
2. la señora
3. las oficinas
4. los billetes
5. el dólar
6. los pesos
7. el cambio
8. la oficina de cambio

Plural of Nouns

1. un señor
2. unas señoras
3. una oficina de cambio
4. un billete
5. unos dólares
6. unos pesos

Chapter 2

Subject Pronouns

1. yo
2. él
3. ellos
4. ella
5. nosotros
6. ellas
7. él
8. ella
9. él
10. ellos
11. ellos
12. ellas
13. yo
14. él
15. ellos
16. ella
17. nosotros
18. ellas
19. él
20. ella
21. él
22. ellos
23. ellos
24. ellas

Formal and Informal Form of "You"

1. tú—your friend Thomas
2. ustedes—your friends Eduardo & Roberto
3. ustedes—your friends Karen & Silvia
4. tú—your friend Elena
5. usted—the agency director, Mrs. García
6. tú—Lupe, your maid
7. ustedes—your mom and dad
8. tú—your son
9. ustedes—Mr. and Mrs. Jones
10. ustedes—Mrs. Jones and Mrs. García
11. tú—your sister
12. usted—the company president
13. usted—your boss
14. ustedes—a group of your teachers

Chapter 3

Present Tense Indicative

1. yo como
2. tú vives
3. nosotros cambiamos
4. ellos necesitan
5. nosotros vivimos
6. ustedes comen
7. él toma
8. yo llevo
9. ella deja
10. usted paga
11. tú hablas
12. ellas hablan

More About Verbs

1. yo tomo
2. usted lleva

3. ellos necesitan
4. tú cambias
5. yo hablo
6. ustedes comen
7. ella vive
8. ellas dejan
9. él camina
10. tú doblas
11. nosostras tomamos

Chapter 4

The Verb Gustar

1. Me gusta la comida mexicana.
2. ¿Te gustan las habitaciones?
3. A ellos, les gusta viajar.
4. Nos gustan las enchiladas.
5. A ella, no le gustan los tacos.
6. A Thomas, no le gusta comer solo.
7. Me gustan los restaurantes buenos.
8. A nosotros nos gustan las habitaciones.
9. A ti no te gusta el desayuno.
10. A los Smith les gusta el hotel.
11. A mí me gusta la comida mexicana.
12. A nosotros nos gusta México.

Chapter 5

Numbers above 100

1. doscientos
2. trescientos cuarenta y cinco
3. cuatrocientos setenta y seis
4. quinientos diez
5. mil
6. novecientos ochenta y tres
7. setecientos uno
8. seiscientos treinta y ocho
9. ochocientos cincuenta y nueve
10. doscientos sesenta y siete

Ways to Express Polite Requests

1. ¿Podría usted decirme dónde hay un buen restaurante?
2. Yo quisiera cambiar cien dólares.
3. Tráigame una cerveza, por favor.
4. ¿Puede usted traerme la cuenta, por favor?
5. ¿Podría usted indicarme dónde está mi habitación?
6. Yo querría alquilar una habitación.
7. Perdón, señora. ¿Dónde está el Hotel Plaza?
8. No se marche, por favor.
9. Llamaré más tarde, gracias.
10. Lo siento, no contesta nadie.
11. ¿Quiere usted traerme la cuenta, por favor?

Chapter 6

Ser and Estar

1. Son las cuatro de la tarde.
2. Thomas y Alberto son hombres de negocios.
3. María es recepcionista.
4. El restaurante está al otro lado de la calle.
5. Thomas está en México.
6. Ana y Luisa son muy amables.
7. Las maletas no son de usted.
8. Elena es la esposa de Thomas.
9. Yo estoy bien, gracias.
10. Hola, Roberto. ¿Cómo estás?

Some Uses of Ser and Estar

1. Yo estoy en el aeropuerto.
2. Nosotros somos de los Estados Unidos.
3. Alberto está en una reunión.
4. El apartamento es de Juan.
5. ¿Qué hora es?
6. El restaurante está cerca del hotel.
7. Está todo bien?
8. El hotel es bastante bueno.
9. Los precios son un poco altos.
10. Thomas es muy inteligente.

Irregular Verbs in the Present Tense

1. ¿Puedo yo reservar una habitación?
2. ¿Quieren ustedes ir al restaurante?
3. Juan y María salen del aeropuerto.
4. Nosotros venimos desde Miami.
5. Ella viene de una reunión.
6. Tú tienes amigos en México.
7. ¿Quieres tú ir al teatro?
8. Nosotros preferimos comer en el hotel.

9. ¿Puedo yo cambiar unos dólares?
10. Thomas tiene muchas maletas.

Chapter 7

Interrogative Words

1. ¿Quién es ese hombre?
2. ¿Cuánto dinero necesitas?
3. ¿Cómo te llamas?
4. ¿Cuándo llega Thomas?
5. ¿Cuánto cuesta la habitación?
6. ¿Quiénes son esas personas?

Contractions Del and Al

1. Voy al aeropuerto.
2. Vengo del hotel.
3. Thomas llamas a la secretaria.
4. ¿Me lleva al hotel?
5. Juan sale de la oficina.
6. Voy a ver al señor García.
7. El restaurante está al otro lado de la calle.

More Irregular Verbs in the Present Tense

1. Yo voy a mi habitación.
2. ¿Dónde ponemos (nosotros) el equipaje?
3. ¿Traes tú las maletas?
4. El botones trae el equipaje.
5. El botones pone el equipaje al lado de la cama.
6. Karen le da una propina al botones.
7. Yo no oigo nada.
8. ¿Qué dices tú?
9. Ellas van a cenar al restaurante.
10. Yo te doy mi número de teléfono.

Chapter 8

Pedir vs. Preguntar

1. Thomas le pregunta a una señora dónde está la oficina de correos.
2. El recepcionista le pide veinticinco pesos por la habitación.
3. El camarero le pregunta qué quiere comer.
4. La policia le pide el pasaporte.
5. Karen le pregunta al botones dónde hay un restaurante.
6. Thomas pide agua mineral con la cena.
7. Karen pide cerveza con la cena.
8. Mario le pregunta al camarero si tienen tacos.

Hacer

1. Yo hago una llamada a larga distancia.
2. Tú haces una reservación en el hotel.
3. Thomas necesita marcar "6" cuando él hace una llamada local.
4. Nosotros hacemos un viaje a Acapulco.
5. Ud. hace muchas llamadas a los Estados Unidos.
6. Ella hace una reservación a nombre de "Karen Santiago".
7. Uds. hacen varias llamadas a su oficina.

Chapter 9

Indirect Object Pronoun

1. Le hablo.
2. Ella me da la dirección.
3. Te traigo una cerveza.
4. El camarero nos llama.
5. Les hago un precio especial.
6. Le pregunto qué quiere comer.
7. El camarero les da el menú.

Mucho, Muy, and Poco

1. La comida es muy buena.
2. Hay mucha gente en el aeropuerto.
3. Thomas trabaja mucho.
4. El hotel es muy caro.
5. México es una ciudad muy grande.
6. Es una ciudad muy interesante.
7. Yo no tengo mucho dinero.
8. Muchas personas viven en Latinoamérica.
9. Karen tiene muchos amigos en México.
10. Thomas toma mucho café.

Chapter 10

Saber vs. Conocer

1. ¿Conoces a mi hermano?
2. No sé dónde está la estación.
3. ¿Saben ustedes el nombre de ese señor?
4. Los Smith no conocen Colombia.

5. ¿Sabes manejar?
6. Juan conoce a todo el mundo aquí.
7. No conozco la ciudad.

Chapter 11

Agreement of Adjectives

1. La habitación es pequeña.
2. Los niños están animados.
3. La información es correcta.
4. La señora está encantada de conocerte.
5. Los cuartos son grandes.
6. El hotel es caro.
7. La comida es buena.

The Present Progressive

1. Juan está hablando por teléfono.
2. Nosotros estamos trabajando en la Argentina.
3. Thomas y Elena están viviendo en un hotel.
4. Yo estoy leyendo un libro muy interesante.
5. Silvia está escribiendo una carta.
6. ¿Por quá estás bebiendo tanto café?
7. Tus amigos están bailando.

Chapter 12

Days of the Week

1. El primer día de la semana es el lunes.
2. El martes es el día antes del miércoles.
3. El domingo es el séptimo día.
4. El cuarto día es el jueves.
5. El martes está entre el lunes y el miércoles.
6. El sábado es el sexto día de la semana.
7. El viernes va después del jueves.

Chapter 13

Stem-Changing Verbs

1. La oficina se cierra a las cuatro.
2. Yo prefiero comer la ensalada.
3. ¿Cuándo vuelves a tu país?
4. ¿Cuándo vienen ustedes a visitarnos?
5. Nosotros no podemos terminar toda la comida.
6. Thomas pide el menú.
7. Karen y Mario juegan al tenis.

Chapter 14

Reflexive Verbs and Pronouns

1. Nosostros nos marchamos.
2. Él se acuesta muy tarde.
3. Ellos se lavan las manos.
4. Tú te vistes rápidamente.
5. Ellas se divierten en la fiesta.
6. Ustedes se sienten mal.
7. Usted se afeita por la mañana.
8. Yo me duermo a las diez de la noche.

Some Common Reflexive Verbs

1. Yo normalmente me despierto a las seis.
2. Entonces, yo me levanto a las seis y me baño.
3. ¿Cómo se llama ese señor?
4. Roberto se divierte mucho en la fiesta.
5. ¿A qué hora se acuestan los niños?
6. ¿No te sientes bien tú?
7. Nosotros nos sentamos aquí.
8. Tú siempre te duermes en las reuniones.
9. Eduardo se pone una camisa blanca.
10. Yo me visto antes de salir de la casa.

Chapter 15

Formal Commands

1. Hable usted más despacio, por favor.
2. Esperen ustedes junto a la puerta.
3. Llame usted más tarde.
4. Vayan ustedes hasta la calle siguiente.
5. Traiga usted la cuenta, por favor.
6. Salgan ustedes del autobús con cuidado.
7. Ponga usted almidón en las camisas.

Present Subjunctive Forms

1. Quiero que usted lave la ropa en agua fría.
2. Quiero que ustedes vengan a verme hoy.
3. Prefiero que los niños no estén solos en la casa.
4. Es necesario que tú me des tu número de teléfono.
5. Espero que alguien conteste el teléfono.
6. Les recomiendo que ustedes no beban el agua.
7. ¿Qué quieres que yo haga ahora?
8. Quiero que tú me digas toda la verdad.

Chapter 16

Preterite of Regular Verbs

1. El año pasado yo visité Chile.
2. ¿Hablaste tú con el farmacéutico?
3. Ellos vivieron dos años en el Perú.
4. Thomas bebió una cerveza.
5. Tú nunca comiste en ese restaurante.
6. ¿Reservó usted una mesa en el restaurante?
7. Yo te vi con Eduardo anoche.
8. ¿Consultó usted a un médico?

Spelling Changes in the Preterite

1. Nosotros fuimos al mar.
2. Roberto y Thomas dijeron que el tour es interesante.
3. Elena no quiso ir a las montañas.
4. Yo ya pagué la cuenta.
5. ¿No durmió usted bien anoche?
6. El policía me pidió el pasaporte.
7. Yo busqué a los niños.
8. Yo empecé a trabajar la semana pasada.
9. Los García leyeron una noticia en el periódico.
10. Nosotros pedimos una botella de vino.
11. Thomas no pudo terminar la comida.
12. ¿Cómo supiste tú la dirección de ella?
13. Nosotros tuvimos una hora libre.

Irregular Verbs in the Preterite

1. Mamá me dio diez mil pesos.
2. Nosotros no dijimos nada.
3. ¿Qué hiciste tú anoche?
4. ¿Dónde puso el botones mi maleta?
5. Elena supo dónde hay un buen mercado.
6. Thomas estuvo en su oficina toda la tarde.
7. Yo no pude encontrar la oficina de correos.

Chapter 17

Para and Por

1. Caminamos por la playa todas las mañanas.
2. Este dinero es para usted.
3. Los Smith salieron para Acapulco.
4. Trabajo por una firma francesa.
5. Thomas vino para trabajar con nosotros.
6. Compré ropa para los niños.
7. Vuelva mañana por la mañana.

Possessive Adjectives

1. su carro
2. mi dinero
3. sus casas
4. mis clientes
5. tu dirección
6. su número de teléfono
7. su esposa
8. nuestras amigas
9. nuestro hotel

Chapter 18

The Imperfect Tense

1. Hacía buen tiempo cuando salimos de excursión.
2. Thomas y Alberto siempre hablaban de negocios.
3. Yo vivía en Madrid cuando conocí a tu padre.
4. Ellos estaban muy cansados cuando llegaron a Acapulco.
5. Nosotros comíamos todos los días en ese restaurante.
6. Tú siempre salías del trabajo a las seis.
7. Yo iba a Cancún todos los años.
8. Las esposa de Roberto era su secretaria.
9. Nosotros íbamos a las montañas con frecuencia.
10. Los padres de Eduardo eran muy ricos.
11. Yo no podía ver muy bien.
12. ¿Siempre viajaban ustedes en autobús?
13. No me gustaba la ciudad donde vivía antes.
14. Elena quería visitar las tiendas.

Verbs like Gustar

1. Me encantan los camarones.
2. A Elena le fastidian los viajes organizados.
3. ¿Te duelen las piernas?
4. Nos faltan treinta mil pesos.
5. A Karen le preocupa la salud de Mario.
6. A los niños no les interesa una representación folklórica.
7. No nos quedan muchos días libres.

Chapter 19

Demonstrative Adjectives and Pronouns

1. esta casa
2. esos hoteles
3. aquellos hombres
4. aquella mujer
5. esta noche
6. esa medicina
7. esta mañana
8. aquel pantalón
9. esas camisas
10. este viaje
11. aquellos autobuses
12. esas montañas

Comparisons of Inequality

1. Estos libros son más interesantes que ésos.
2. La comida en este restaurante es mejor que la comida en el hotel.
3. Thomas es mayor que Elena.
4. Este pañuelo es más elegante que ése.
5. Silvia es menor que Elena.
6. Tú hablas inglés mejor que yo.
7. Ahora me siento peor que antes.
8. Aquellos libros eran más baratos que éstos.

Chapter 20

The Meaning of Hay

1. No hay nadie aquí que pueda contestar.
2. Había mucha gente en la calle.
3. Thomas y Elena estaban en Acapulco.
4. Thomas es un hombre de negocios.
5. Los niños están en casa.
6. Hay dos fiestas esta noche.
7. ¿Hay un banco cerca de aquí?
8. Karen está en el mercado.

Uses of Lo

1. the important thing = lo importante
2. I don't understand it. = No lo comprendo.
3. the best thing = lo mejor
4. the most interesting thing = lo más interesante
5. I don't know. = No lo sé.
6. Say it. = Dígalo.
7. Leave it. = Déjelo.

Chapter 21

Direct Object Pronouns

1. Lo tengo aquí.
2. No la conozco.
3. Ella te llama.
4. Nosotros los compramos.
5. Ellos me dan el regalo.
6. Mario las visita.
7. Karen nos escribe.

Chapter 22

Subjunctive After Impersonal Expressions

1. Es importante que usted evite las comidas pesadas.
2. ¿Es necesario que yo tome alguna medicina especial?
3. Es preciso que nosotros vayamos al mercado hoy.
4. Es preferible que ustedes vengan conmigo al mercado.
5. ¡Es increíble que tú compres tanto!
6. ¡Es terrible que ellos no puedan acompañarnos!
7. Es posible que ellos no tengan pescado hoy.

The Subjunctive in Adverbial Clauses

1. Iremos a España cuando nosotros terminemos el trabajo aquí.
2. Te llamaré tan pronto como llegue al hotel.
3. No te olvides de comprar la carne cuando estés en el mercado.
4. En cuanto Thomas encuentre un apartamento, va a traer a su familia.
5. Siempre compro regalos cuando yo estoy en Acapulco.
6. Elena no quiere manejar mientras ella esté en México.
7. Usted no puede marcharse hasta que consiga un pasaporte.

8. Cuando voy de vacaciones, me gusta viajar en autobús.
9. Karen siempre le llama a Mario tan pronto como llega al hotel.

Chapter 23

Irregular *tú* Commands

1. Prepara la comida.
2. Compra las verduras.
3. Hazlo todo.
4. Ve a la lavandería.
5. Ven conmigo.
6. Ten paciencia.
7. Pon el vino en la mesa.
8. Sal temprano.
9. Recoge la mesa.

Chapter 24

Preterite vs. Imperfect

1. El sábado pasado, yo estaba en Mérida cuando llegó mi amigo.
2. Nosotros íbamos todos los días a la playa.
3. Ayer yo vi a Elena en el mercado.
4. Mi marido siempre me llamaba a las cuatro de la tarde.
5. Yo conocí a Eduardo en una fiesta.
6. Ayer yo recibí seis llamadas telefónicas.
7. ¿Les gustó la representación folklórica?

Comparisons of Equality

1. Mario tiene tantos hijos como Thomas.
2. Elena es tan alta como Thomas.
3. Thomas maneja tan rápido como yo.
4. Tú tienes tantas camisas como él.
5. Ese vestido es tan elegante como éste.
6. Mis trajes son tan viejos como los tuyos.
7. Thomas tiene tantos trajes como yo.
8. Karen tiene tantas blusas como Elena.
9. Silvia no necesita comprar tanta comida como Karen.

Chapter 25

The Past Participle

1. ¿Ha llegado una transferencia desde los Estados Unidos?
2. He abierto una cuenta en el banco.
3. Karen ha dicho que quiere cheques de viaje.
4. Elena ha hecho un depósito.
5. El libro fue escrito por mi profesor.
6. Los niños han roto la ventana.
7. ¿Has visto a Mario hoy?
8. Silvia todavía no ha vuelto de la reunión.
9. Eduardo me ha llamado por teléfono.

Irregular Past Participles

1. Roberto me ha dicho que usted va a trabajar con nosotros.
2. Los padres de Thomas le han escrito una carta.
3. Lupe, ¿has hecho las camas hoy?
4. Los Smith han vuelto de vacaciones hoy.
5. ¿Por qué no has abierto la puerta?
6. Nosotros no hemos visto todavía esa representación.
7. Elena y yo hemos descubierto una tienda maravillosa.

The Present Perfect Tense

1. El dinero no ha llegado todavía al banco.
2. Thomas ha abierto una cuenta de ahorros.
3. Elena y Silvia no han vuelto del mercado.
4. ¿Qué has hecho tú?
5. Ustedes han depositado cinco millones de pesos.
6. Nosotros hemos recibido una transferencia desde Chicago.
7. Yo no he visto a Thomas.

Chapter 26

Stem and Spelling Changes in the Present Subjunctive

1. Thomas quiere que el camarero le traiga agua.
2. El médico me dice que yo tome esta pastilla.
3. Es preferible que ustedes vayan con un tour organizado.

4. Elena insiste en que Lupe haga todo el trabajo hoy.
5. Recomiendo que tú busques un buen mecánico.
6. ¡Es terrible que nosotros no tengamos ni un momento libre esta semana!
7. ¡Es ridículo que ustedes no acepten tarjetas de crédito!
8. Quiero que tú me expliques algo.

Subjunctive After Verbs of Willing

1. Elena quiere que el mecánico revise el aceite.
2. El mecánico no quiere que yo pague con tarjeta de crédito.
3. Roberto prohibe que sus hijos manejen el carro nuevo.
4. Karen pide que el mecánico le ponga agua en la batería.
5. Thomas insiste en que Elena vuelva a casa ahora mismo.
6. El médico me recomienda que yo duerma un mínimo de siete horas cada noche.
7. Los Smith quieren encontrar una casa en el centro.
8. Silvia quiere comprar unas salchichas.

Chapter 27

Holidays, Seasons, and Months

1. El verano es una estación; no es un día festivo.
2. El otoño es una estación; no es un mes.
3. Octubre es un mes; no es una estación.
4. El viento no tiene que ver con los cumpleaños.
5. Noviembre no tiene que ver con el tiempo.
6. Diciembre no tiene que ver con la primavera.

Chapter 28

The Conditional Tense

1. Thomas dijo que hablaría con Elena.
2. Ella comería en un restaurante mexicano.
3. Nosotros viviríamos en México por un año.
4. Ellos dirían que Roberto es su amigo.
5. Ellas harían un buen almuerzo para ti.
6. Yo podría visitar Acapulco.
7. Tú saldrías del trabajo a las seis.
8. Karen tendría que reservar cuatro puestos.
9. Mario vendría a Taxco con Karen.

Irregular Verbs in the Conditional Tense

1. Por favor, ¿podría usted decirme la hora?
2. Pensé que los padres de Thomas vendrían para las fiestas de Navidad.
3. Yo querría cambiar cien dólares, por favor.
4. El mecánico me dijo que él me pondría aire en la rueda.
5. ¿Sería usted tan amable de indicarme el camino?
6. La permanente le daría más volumen.
7. No, es que le daría un poco más de volumen.
8. Eso le vendría bien a mi marido.
9. Se está quedando casi calvo.
10. A mi marido, no le gustarían tantos rizos.
11. ¿Qué harías tú en mi lugar?

Chapter 29

The Subjunctive After Verbs of Emotion

1. Me alegro de que usted pueda acompañarnos el viernes.
2. Es una lástima que a ustedes no les guste el teatro.
3. Me fastidia que ellos no sirvan carne en este restaurante.
4. ¿Te sorprende que las entradas sean tan caras?
5. ¡Me asombra que tú conozcas a mis primos en Chicago!
6. Siento que nosotros no tengamos más tiempo libre para ver la ciudad.
7. Espero que nosotras terminemos el trabajo pronto.

Subjunctive in Expressions of Doubt

1. Estoy segura que quedan entradas.
2. Es dudoso que hayan dos asientos juntos.
3. Dudo que él pueda pasar por su hotel.

4. Thomas no cree que Roberto y Silvia quieran acompañarlos al teatro.
5. Es cierto que muchas personas van a las funciones en Bellas Artes.
6. Creo que los actores son de Buenos Aires.
7. No es cierto que la directora hable inglés.
8. Es verdad que mis padres vienen para las fiestas de Navidad.

Chapter 30

Reciprocal Actions

1. Thomas y Elena se llaman frecuentemente por teléfono.
2. Nosotros casi nunca nos escribimos.
3. Eduardo y Thomas se veían todos los días en la oficina.
4. Silvia y yo raramente nos hablamos.
5. ¿Se conocen ustedes?
6. Mi marido y yo nos queremos mucho.

Irregular Verbs in the Future Tense

1. Ustedes tendrán que terminar el trabajo mañana.
2. Nostros querremos causar una buena impresión.
3. El vuelo saldrá a las tres y cuarto.
4. Yo pondré el maletín debajo de mi asiento.
5. ¿Sabrá la directora que no hemos terminado?
6. ¿Qué dirá mi esposo cuando me vea con una permanente?
7. Ustedes podrán llamarme desde el aeropuerto.
8. ¿Vendrán Elena y los niños al aeropuerto con Thomas?
9. ¿Habrá tiempo suficiente para documentar el equipaje?
10. Thomas hará otro viaje al Ecuador en octubre.

Index of Grammar Topics

CHAPTER 1

Story

	Spanish	English
Karen	Necesito cambiar dólares por pesos.	*I need to change dollars for pesos.*
Karen	¿Dónde está la oficina de cambio?	*Where is the exchange office?*
Empleada	La oficina de cambio está a la vuelta.	*The exchange office is around the corner.*
Karen	Necesito cambiar unos dólares.	*I need to change some dollars.*
Cajero	¿Cuántos quiere cambiar?	*How many do you want to change?*
Cajero	El cambio está a tres pesos por dólar.	*The exchange rate is three pesos to the dollar.*
Karen	Treinta dólares.	*Thirty dollars.*
Cajero	¿Cómo los quiere?	*How do you want them?*
Karen	En billetes grandes, por favor.	*In large bills, please.*

Action

	Spanish	English
Thomas	Perdón, señora.	*Excuse me, ma'am..*
Empleada	¿Dígame?	*May I help you?*
Thomas	¿Dónde puedo cambiar unos dólares?	*Where can I change some money?.*
Empleada	La oficina de cambio está a la vuelta.	*The exchange office is right around the corner.*
Thomas	Gracias.	*Thanks.*
Thomas	Señor, necesito cambiar unos dólares.	*Sir, I need to change some dollars.*
Cajero	¿Cuántos?	*How many?*
Thomas	Treinta dólares.	*Thirty dollars.*
Cajero	El cambio está a tres pesos por dólar. Entonces, son noventa pesos. ¿Cómo los quiere?	*The exchange rate is three pesos to the dollar. So, that makes ninely pesos. How do you want them?*
Thomas	En billetes grandes, por favor.	*In large bills, please.*
Cajero	Aquí tiene.	*Here you are.*
Thomas	Muchas gracias.	*Thank you very much.*

CHAPTER 2

Story

	Spanish	English
Karen	Para ir al hotel, necesito tomar un taxi.	*To go to the hotel, I need to take a taxi.*
Karen	Buenos días. ¿Está libre?	*Is this taxi free?*
Taxista	Sí. ¿Adónde quiere ir?	*Yes. Where do you want to go?*
Karen	¿Por cuánto me lleva al Hotel Internacional?	*How much do you want to take me to the Hotel Internacional?*
Taxista	¿Cuántos pasajeros?	*How many passengers?*
Karen	Yo sola.	*Just me.*
Taxista	Treinta pesos.	*Thirty pesos.*
Karen	No, es demasiado. Le doy veinte.	*No, that's too much. I'll give you twenty.*
Taxista	No, no puedo por menos de veinticinco.	*I can't do it for less than twenty five.*
Karen	De acuerdo.	*O.K.*
Taxista	Ponga las maletas aquí atrás.	*Put your luggage here in the back.*
Karen	Gracias.	*Thanks.*
Taxista	De nada.	*You're welcome.*

Action

	Spanish	English
Thomas	Taxi, ¿está libre?	*Is this taxi free?*
Taxista	Sí. ¿A dónde quiere ir?	*Yes. Where do you want to go?*
Thomas	¿Por cuánto me lleva al Hotel Internacional?	*How much do you want to take me to the Hotel Internacional?*
Taxista	¿Cuántos pasajeros?	*How many passengers?*
Thomas	Yo solo.	*Just me.*
Taxista	Treinta pesos.	*Thirty pesos.*
Thomas	No, es demasiado. Le doy veinte.	*No, that's too much. I'll give you twenty.*
Taxista	No, no puedo por menos de veinticinco.	*I can't do it for less than twenty five.*
Thomas	De acuerdo.	*O.K.*
Taxista	Ponga las maletas aquí atrás.	*Put your luggage here in the back.*
Thomas	Gracias.	*Thanks.*

CHAPTER 3

Story

	Spanish	English
Karen	Buenos días. Tengo reservada una habitación a nombre de Karen Santiago.	*Good morning. I have a room reserved here in the name of Karen Santiago.*
Recepcionista	Lo siento, pero no encuentro nada aquí.	*I'm sorry, but I don't find any record of it.*
Karen	Necesito una habitación para una persona, con baño privado. ¿Cuánto cuesta?	*I need a room for one person with a private bath. How much will that be?*
Recepcionista	¿Por cuántos días?	*For how many days?*
Karen	No sé. Unos quince días.	*I don't know. About fifteen days.*
Recepcionista	Entonces le podemos hacer un precio especial. Cincuenta pesos diarios.	*Then we can offer you a special price. Fifty pesos a day.*
Recepcionista	Este precio incluye el desayuno.	*This price includes breakfast.*
Karen	¿No tienen habiatciones más baratas?	*Don't you have less expensive rooms?*
Recepcionista	Hay habiatciones más pequeñas pero sin baño privado.	*There are smaller rooms, but they don't have private baths.*
Karen	Déjelo, prefiero pagar un poco más y tener baño privado.	*Leave it, I prefer to pay a little more and have a private bathroom.*

Action

	Spanish	English
Thomas	Buenos días. Tengo reservada una habitación a nombre de Thomas Smith.	*Good morning. I have a room reserved here in the name of Thomas Smith.*
Recepcionista	Lo siento, pero no encuentro nada aquí.	*I'm sorry, but I don't find any record of it.*
Thomas	Necesito una habitación para una persona, con baño privado. ¿Cuánto cuesta?	*I need a room for one person with a private bath. How much will that be?*
Recepcionista	¿Por cuántos días?	*For how many days?*
Thomas	No sé. Unos quince días.	*I don't know. About fifteen days.*
Recepcionista	Entonces le podemos hacer un precio especial. Cincuenta pesos diarios. Este precio incluye el desayuno.	*Then we can offer you a special price. Fifty pesos a day. This price includes breakfast.*
Thomas	¿No tienen habitaciones más baratas?	*Don't you have less expensive rooms?*
Recepcionista	Hay habitaciones más pequeñas pero sin baño privado.	*There are smaller rooms, but they don't have private baths.*
Thomas	Déjelo, prefiero pagar un poco más y tener un baño privado.	*Leave it, I prefer to pay a little more and have a private bathroom.*

CHAPTER 4

Story

	Spanish	*English*
Botones	¿Dónde pongo las maletas, señorita?	*Where should I put the suitcases, miss?*
Karen	Póngalas al lado de la cama, por favor.	*Put them next to the bed, please.*
Botones	¿Está todo bien? ¿Necesita algo más?	*Is everything alright? Do you need anything else?*
Karen	Sí, espere un momento. No se marche. Necesito jabón, toallas y agua mineral.	*Yes, wait a minute. I need soap, towels, and mineral water.*
Botones	Muy bien. Ahora se lo traigo todo.	*Fine. I'll bring them to you right away.*
Karen	Tengo hambre. ¿Puede decirme dónde puedo comer cerca de aquí?	*Just a minute. Don't go. Can you tell me where I can eat near here?*
Botones	¿Prefiere comida norteamericana o mexicana?	*Do you prefer American food or Mexican food?*
Karen	Me gustaría comer algo mexicano.	*I'd like to eat something Mexican.*
Botones	Hay un restaurante bastante bueno al otro lado de la calle. Se llama "El Tampiqeuño.	*There's a fairly good restaurant right across the street. It's called El Tampiqueño.*
Karen	Muchas gracias. Aquí tiene.	*Thanks a lot. Here you are.*

Action

	Spanish	*English*
Botones	¿Dónde pongo las maletas, señor?	*Where should I put the suitcases, sir?*
Thomas	Póngalas al lado de la cama, por favor.	*Put them next to the bed, please.*
Botones	¿Está todo bien? ¿Necesita algo más?	*Is everything alright? Do you need anything else?*
Thomas	Sí, espere un momento. Necesito jabón, toallas y agua mineral.	*Yes, wait a minute. I need soap, towels, and mineral water.*
Botones	Muy bien. Ahora se lo traigo todo.	*Fine. I'll bring them to you right away.*
Thomas	Un momento. No se marche. ¿Puede decirme dónde puedo comer cerca de aquí?	*Just a minute. Don't go. Can you tell me where I can eat near here?*
Botones	¿Prefiere comida norteamericana o mexicana?	*Do you prefer American food or Mexican food?*
Thomas	Me gustaría comer algo mexicano.	*I'd like to eat something Mexican.*
Botones	Hay un restaurante bastante bueno al otro lado de la calle. Se llama "El Tampiqueño".	*There's a fairly good restaurant right across the street. It's called El Tampiqueño.*
Thomas	Muchas gracias. Aquí tiene.	*Thanks a lot. Here you are.*

CHAPTER 5

Story

	Spanish	*English*
Operadora	¿Bueno?	*Hello?*
Karen	Quiero hacer una llamada a Estados Unidos, por favor.	*I want to make a call to the United States, please.*
Operadora	¿De persona a persona?	*Person to person?*
Karen	Sí, con el señor Mario Santiago, por cobrar, por favor.	*Yes, with Mr. Mario Santiago, collect, please.*
Operadora	Y ¿cómo se llama usted?	*And what is your name?*
Karen	Karen, Karen Santiago.	*Karen, Karen Santiago.*
Operadora	¿El número, por favor?	*The number, please?*
Karen	Es el 423-450-2105.	*It's 423-450-2105.*
Operadora	Ahora mismo.	*Right away.*
Operadora	Lo siento, no contesta nadie. ¿Quiere que insista?	*I'm sorry. No one answers. Do you want me to keep trying?*
Karen	Sí, por favor.	*Yes, please.*
Operadora	Todavía no contesta nadie. ¿Quiere volver a llamar más tarde?	*There's still no answer. Would you like to call back later?*
Karen	Está bien. Llamaré más tarde. Gracias.	*Alright. I'll call later. Thanks.*
Operadora	No hay de que. Adiós.	*Don't mention it. Good-bye.*
Karen	Adiós.	*Good-bye.*

Action

	Spanish	*English*
Thomas	Quiero hacer una llamada a Estados Unidos, por favor.	*I want to make a call to the United States, please.*
Operadora	¿Por cobrar?	*Do you want to reverse the charges?*
Thomas	Sí.	*Yes.*
Operadora	¿El número, por favor?	*What's the number, please?*
Thomas	Es el 615-974-2311. De persona a persona, con la señora Elena Smith.	*It's 615-974-2311. Person to person, to Mrs. Elena Smith.*
Operadora	Ahora mismo.	*Right away.*
Operadora	Lo siento. No contesta nadie. ¿Quiere que insista?	*I'm sorry. No one answers. Do you want me to keep trying?*
Thomas	No, gracias. Llamaré más tarde.	*No, thanks. I'll call later.*

CHAPTER 6

Story

	Spanish	*English*
Karen	¿Puede decirme cómo llamar directamente dentro de la ciudad?	*Can you tell me how to make a local phone call?*
Operadora	Sí, señorita. Marque el númer seis primero, y después el número que usted desee.	*Yes, miss. Dial number 6 first, then the number that you want.*
Secretaria 2	Bueno.	*Hello.*
Karen	¿Está el señor Garcia?	*Is Mr. García in?*
Secretaria 2	¿De parte de quién?	*Who's calling, please?*
Karen	De parte de Karen Santiago.	*Karen Santiago.*
Secretaria 2	Lo siento. El señor Garcia no está en su oficina; está en una reunión.	*I'm sorry. Mr. García is in a meeting.*
Secretaria 2	¿Quiere dejar un recado?	*Do you want to leave a message?*
Karen	Sí, dígale que me llame al Hotel Internacional.	*Yes, tell him to call me at the Hotel Internacional.*
Karen	Estoy aquí hasta las nueve.	*I'll be here until nine.*
Secretaria 2	¡Cómo no! ¿Algo más?	*Of course. Anything else?*
Karen	Nada más, gracias. Adiós.	*That's all, thanks. Good-bye.*
Secretaria 2	Muy bien. Adiós.	*Alright. Good-bye.*

Action

	Spanish	*English*
Thomas	¿Puede decirme cómo llamar directamente dentro de la ciudad?	*Can you tell me how to make a local phone call?*
Operadora	Sí, señor. Marque el número 6 primero, y después el número que usted desee.	*Yes, sir. Dial number 6 first, then the number that you want.*
Thomas	Gracias.	*Thanks.*
Thomas	¿Está el señor García?	*Is Mr. García in?*
Secretaria 2	¿De parte de quién?	*Who's calling, please?*
Thomas	De parte de Thomas Smith.	*Thomas Smith.*
Secretaria 2	Lo siento. El señor García está en una reunión. ¿Quiere dejar un recado?	*I'm sorry. Mr. García is in a meeting. Do you want to leave a message?*
Thomas	Sí, dígale que me llame al Hotel Internacional. Estoy aquí hasta las nueve.	*Yes, tell him to call me at the Hotel Internacional. I'll be here until nine.*
Secretaria 2	¡Cómo no! ¿Algo más?	*Of course. Anything else?*
Thomas	Nada más, gracias. Adiós.	*That's all, thanks. Good-bye.*

CHAPTER 7

Story

	Spanish	English
Camarero	Buenas noches. ¿Espera usted a alguien?	*Good evening. Are you waiting for someone?*
Karen	No, estoy sola.	*No, I'm alone.*
Camarero	¿Dónde quiere sentarse?	*Where do you want to sit?*
Karen	Cerca de la ventana, por favor.	*Near the window, please.*
Camarero	¿Desea tomar algo antes de pedir?	*Do you want something to drink before you order?*
Karen	Sí, tráigame una cerveza fría, por favor.	*Yes, bring me a cold beer.*
Camarero	¿Qué desea comer?	*What do you want to eat?*
Karen	En el almuerzo sólo comí una ensalada verde. Tengo mucha hambre.	*For lunch I only had a green salad. I'm very hungry.*
Karen	Quiero un consomé de pollo y las enchiladas suizas.	*I want chicken soup, enchiladas suizas, and a green salad.*
Camarero	Muy bien.	*Very well.*
Camarero	Qué disfrute su cena.	*Enjoy your dinner.*
Karen	Gracias.	*Thank you.*
Camarero	¿Quiere tomar algo de postre?	*Would you like something for dessert?*
Karen	No gracias. Tráigame la cuenta, por favor.	*No thanks. Bring me the bill, please.*

Action

	Spanish	English
Camarero	Buenas noches. ¿Espera usted a alguien?	*Good evening. Are you waiting for someone?*
Thomas	No, estoy solo.	*No, I'm alone.*
Camarero	¿Dónde quiere sentarse?	*Where do you want to sit?*
Thomas	Cerca de la ventana, por favor.	*Near the window, please.*
Camarero	¿Desea tomar algo antes de pedir?	*Do you want something to drink before you order?*
Thomas	Sí, tráigame una cerveza fría.	*Yes, bring me a cold beer.*
Camarero	¿Qué desea comer?	*What do you want to eat?*
Thomas	Quiero un consomé de pollo, las enchiladas suizas y una ensalada verde.	*I want chicken soup, enchiladas suizas, and a green salad.*
Camarero	Muy bien.	*Very well.*
Camarero	¿Quiere tomar algo de postre?	*Would you like something for dessert?*
Thomas	No gracias. Tráigame la cuenta, por favor.	*No thanks. Bring me the bill, please.*

CHAPTER 8

Story

	Spanish	English
Karen	Creo que me he perdido.	*I think I'm lost.*
Karen	Perdone, señora, ¿puede decirme dónde está la oficina de correos?	*Excuse me, ma'am. Can you tell me where the post office is?*
Señora	No está muy lejos. Está en la calle Bolívar.	*It's not far from here. It's on Bolívar Street.*
Karen	¿Cómo puedo llegar hasta allá?	*How can I get there from here?*
Señora	Siga todo derecho hasta la calle Nogales.	*Go straight until you get to Nogales Street.*
Señora	Entonces, doble a la izquierda y camine dos cuadras hasta la calle Bolívar. Verá usted la oficina en la esquina.	*Then, turn left and walk two blocks to Bolívar Street. You'll see the post office on the corner.*
Karen	¿Y sabe usted a qué hora se cierra la oficina?	*And do you know what time the office closes?*
Señora	Creo que se cierra a las cuatro de la tarde.	*I think it closes at four p.m.*
Karen	Muy amable. Gracias.	*You've been very kind. Thank you.*
Señora	De nada.	*You're welcome.*

Action

	Spanish	English
Thomas	Perdone, señora, ¿puede decirme dónde está la oficina de correos?	*Excuse me, ma'am. Can you tell me where the post office is?*
Señora	No está muy lejos. Está en la calle Bolívar.	*It's not far from here. It's on Bolívar Street.*
Thomas	¿Cómo puedo llegar hasta allá?	*How can I get there from here?*
Señora	Siga todo derecho hasta la calle Nogales.	*Go straight until you get to Nogales Street.*
Señora	Entonces, doble a la izquierda y camine dos cuadras hasta la calle Bolívar. Verá usted la oficina en la esquina.	*Then, turn left and walk two blocks to Bolívar Street. You'll see the post office on the corner.*
Thomas	¿Y sabe usted a qué hora se cierra la oficina?	*And do you know what time the office closes?*
Señora	Creo que se cierra a las cuatro de la tarde.	*I think it closes at four p.m.*
Thomas	Muy amable. Gracias.	*You've been very kind. Thank you.*
Señora	De nada.	*You're welcome.*

CHAPTER 9

Story

	Spanish	English
Karen	¿Puede indicarme dónde queda la oficina del señor González?	*Can you tell me where Mr. González's office is?*
Recepcionista 2	Está en el tercer piso, al final del pasillo a la derecha.	*It's on the third floor, at the end of the hall on the right.*
Recepcionista 2	El ascensor está a su izquierda.	*The elevator is on your left.*
Karen	Gracias, pero prefiero subir andando.	*Thanks, but I prefer to walk up.*
Karen	¿Dónde quedan las escaleras?	*Where are the stairs?*
Recepcionista 2	Detrás de usted.	*Behind you.*
Karen	¿Está el señor González?	*Is Mr. González here?*
Secretaria 1	No. Se ha equivocado de puerta.	*No. You've made a mistake.*
Secretaria 1	Sí usted busca el señor González, tiene que llamar en la puerta siguiente.	*If you're looking for Mr. González, you have to go next door.*
Karen	¿Es ésta la oficina del Sr. González?	*Is this Mr. González's office?*
Secretaria 2	Sí. ¿Es usted la señora Santiago?	*Yes. Are you Mrs. Santiago?*
Karen	Sí. Soy Karen Santiago.	*Yes. I'm Karen Santiago.*
Secretaria 2	Pase. El Sr. González la está esperando.	*Come in. Mr. González is waiting for you.*
Thomas	¿Puede indicarme dónde queda la oficina del Sr. González?	*Can you tell me where Mr. González's office is?*
Recepcionista 2	Está en el tercer piso, al final del pasillo a la derecha. El ascensor está a su izquierda.	*It's on the third floor, at the end of the hall on the right. The elevator is on your left.*

Action

	Spanish	English
Thomas	Gracias, pero prefiero subir andando. ¿Dónde están las escaleras?	*Thanks, but I prefer to walk up. Where are the stairs?*
Recepcionista 2	Detrás de usted.	*Behind you.*
Thomas	¿Está el Sr. González?	*Is Mr. González here?*
Secretaria 1	No. Se ha equivocado de puerta. Tiene que llamar en la puerta siguiente.	*No. You've made a mistake. You have to go next door.*
Thomas	¿Es ésta la oficina del Sr. González?	*Is this Mr. González's office?*
Secretaria 2	Sí. ¿Es usted el Sr. Smith? Pase. El Sr. González lo está esperando.	*Yes. Are you Mr. Smith? Come in. Mr. González is waiting for you.*

CHAPTER 10

Story

	Spanish	English
Silvia	Hola, Karen. ¿Cómo estás?	*Hello, Karen. How are you?*
Karen	Bien, gracias. Y tú, ¿qué tal estás?	*Just fine, thanks. And you, how are you doing?*
Silvia	Ya ves. Trabajando como siempre.	*As you can see. Working like always.*
Silvia	¿Qué tal el viaje?	*How was your trip?*
Karen	Muy bien, gracias.	*Very nice, thanks.*
Silvia	¿Conoces a mi socio, Eduardo Gutiérrez?	*Do you know my partner, Eduardo Gutiérrez?*
Karen	Encantada de conocerlo.	*I'm glad to meet you.*
Eduardo	Igualmente. Silvia me dice que va a trabajar con nosotros. Me alegro.	*The pleasure's mine. Roberto tells me you're going to work with us. I'm pleased.*
Karen	Pues sí, mi intención es quedarme aquí un año por lo menos.	*Well, yes, my intention is to stay here for at least a year.*
Silvia	¿Vas a traer a tu familia?	*Are you going to have your family join you?*
Karen	Claro. Mario tiene ganas de venir...	*Of course. Mario wants to come...*
Karen	...pero primero tengo que encontrar un apartamento.	*...but first I have to find an apartment.*
Silvia	Si quieres, puedo acompañarte a la inmobiliaria.	*If you want, I can go with you to the rental agency.*
Karen	Sí, y me puedes enseñar la ciudad.	*Yes, and you can show me the city.*

Action

	Spanish	English
Roberto	Hola, Thomas. ¿Cómo estás? ¿Qué tal el viaje?	*Hello, Thomas. How are you? How was your trip?*
Thomas	Muy bien, gracias. Y tú, ¿qué tal estás?	*Just fine, thanks. And you, how are you doing?*
Roberto	Ya ves. Trabajando, como siempre. ¿Conoces a mi socio, Eduardo Gutiérrez?	*As you can see. Working like always. Do you know my partner, Eduardo Gutiérrez?*
Thomas	Encantado de conocerlo.	*I'm glad to meet you.*
Eduardo	Igualmente. Roberto me dice que usted va a trabajar con nosotros. Me alegro.	*The pleasure's mine. Roberto tells me you're going to work with us. I'm pleased.*
Thomas	Pues sí, mi intención es quedarme aquí un año por lo menos.	*Well, yes, my intention is to stay here for at least a year.*
Roberto	¿Vas a traer a tu mujer?	*Are you going to have your wife join you?*
Thomas	Claro. Elena tiene ganas de venir, pero primero tengo que encontrar un apartamento.	*Of course. Elena wants to come, but first I have to find an apartment.*
Eduardo	Tengo tiempo libre el viernes. Si quiere, puedo acompañarlo a la inmobiliaria.	*I have some free time on Friday. If you want, I can go with you to the rental agency.*

CHAPTER 11

Story

	Spanish	English
Silvia	¡Encantada de verte, Karen! Pasa.	*Happy to see you, Karen! Come in.*
Silvia	¿Cómo está la familia?	*How's your family?*
Karen	Están todos bien, gracias.	*They're all fine, thanks.*
Silvia	¿Cuándo va a venir Mario?	*When is Mario coming?*
Karen	Mario viene dentro de dos semanas, y traerá a los niños.	*Mario is coming within the next two weeks and he'll bring the children with him.*
Silvia	Será estupendo volver a verlos.	*It'll be great to see them again.*
Silvia	¿Conoces a todos los invitados?	*Do you know all the guests?*
Karen	A algunos. ¿Quién es la mujer que baila con Roberto?	*Some of them. And, who's the woman dancing with Roberto?*
Silvia	Es mi hermana menor. Vive en Mérida, pero está aquí de visita un par de días.	*She's my younger sister. She lives in Mérida, but she's here visiting for a couple of days.*
Karen	Y ¿quién es el que está en el balcón conversando con Eduardo?	*And, who is the man on the balcony talking to Eduardo?*
Silvia	Es su primo. es abogado y también da clases en la universidad.	*It's his cousin. He's a lawyer and he also teaches at the university.*
Karen	Parece que la fiesta está muy animada.	*It looks like the party's very lively.*

Action

	Spanish	English
Silvia	¡Encantada de verte, Thomas! Pasa. ¿Cómo está la familia? ¿Cuándo va a venir Elena?	*Happy to see you, Thomas! Come in. How's your family? When is Elena coming?*
Thomas	Están todos bien, gracias. Elena viene dentro de dos semanas y traerá a los niños.	*They're all fine, thanks. Elena is coming within the next two weeks and she brings the children with her.*
Silvia	Será estupendo volver a verlos. ¿Conoces a todos los invitados?	*It'll be great to see them again. Do you know all the guests?*
Thomas	A algunos. Y ¿quién es la mujer que está bailando con Roberto?	*Some of them. And, who's the woman dancing with Roberto?*
Silvia	Es mi hermana menor. Vive en Mérida, pero está aquí de visita un par de días.	*She's my younger sister. She lives in Mérida, but she's here visiting for a couple of days.*
Thomas	Y ¿quién es el que está en el balcón conversando con Eduardo?	*And, who is the man on the balcony talking to Eduardo?*
Silvia	Es su primo. Es abogado y también da clases en la universidad.	*It's his cousin. He's a lawyer and he also teaches at the university.*
Thomas	Parece que la fiesta está muy animada.	*It looks like the party's very lively.*

CHAPTER 12

Story

	Spanish	*English*
Karen	¿Podemos vernos mañana por la mañana?	*Can we meet tomorrow morning?*
Cliente	¿A qué hora le conviene a usted?	*What's a convenient time for you?*
Karen	¿Entre las diez y las once?	*Between ten and eleven?*
Cliente	Es un poco difícil para mí.	*That's a little difficult for me.*
Cliente	¿Qué le parece el martes por la tarde? ¿Le parece bien a las cuatro?	*What about Tuesday in the afternoon? Would four o'clock be alright?*
Karen	El martes me parece un buen día, pero tengo que ir a Cuernavaca por la mañana.	*Tuesday is a good day for me, but I have to go to Cuernavaca in the morning.*
Karen	Trataré de estar aquí de vuelta antes de las cuatro.	*I'll try to be back here before four.*
Karen	Depende del tráfico. Usted sabe el problema que hay a esa hora.	*It depends on the traffic. You know what problems there are at that time.*
Cliente	Sí, comprendo. Los embotellamientos so terribles a veces.	*Yes, I understand. The traffic jams are horrible sometimes.*
Cliente	No se preocupe si llega un poco más tarde. Voy a estar en mi oficina hasta las seis.	*Don't worry if you get here a bit late. I'm going to be at the office until six.*
Cliente	Podemos tomar una copa a esa hora y hablar del tema, si le parece.	*We could have a drink then and talk about the matter, if that sounds alright to you.*
Karen	Es una buena idea.	*That's a good idea.*
Karen	Nos vemos entonces.	*We'll see each other then.*
Cliente	Hasta luego.	*See you then.*

CHAPTER 12

Action

	Spanish	English
Thomas	¿Podemos vernos mañana por la mañana?	*Can we meet tomorrow morning?*
Cliente	¿A qué hora le conviene a usted?	*What's a convenient time for you?*
Thomas	¿Entre las diez y las once?	*Between ten and eleven?*
Cliente	Es un poco difícil para mí. ¿Qué le parece el martes por la tarde? ¿Le parece bien a las cuatro?	*That's a little difficult for me. What about Tuesday in the afternoon? Would four o'clock be alright?*
Thomas	El martes me parece un buen día, pero tengo que ir a Cuernavaca por la mañana.	*Tuesday is a good day for me, but I have to go to Cuernavaca in the morning.*
Thomas	Trataré de estar aquí de vuelta antes de las cuatro.	*I'll try to be back here before four.*
Thomas	Depende del tráfico. Usted sabe el problema que hay a esa hora.	*It depends on the traffic. You know what problems there are at that time.*
Cliente	Sí, comprendo. Los embotellamientos son terribles a veces.	*Yes, I understand. The traffic jams are horrible sometimes.*
Cliente	No se preocupe si llega un poco más tarde. Voy a estar en mi oficina hasta las seis.	*Don't worry if you get here a bit late. I'm going to be at the office until six.*
Cliente	Podemos tomar una copa a esa hora y hablar del tema, si le parece.	*We could have a drink then and talk about the matter, if that sounds alright to you.*
Thomas	Es una buena idea. Nos vemos entonces.	*That's a good idea. We'll see each other then.*

CHAPTER 13

Story

	Spanish	English
Karen	¿Tiene algo para el dolor de estómago?	*Do you have something for a stomach ache?*
Farmacéutico	¿Qué le ocurre?	*What's wrong with you?*
Karen	No lo sé. Comí algo anoche y no me siento muy bien.	*I don't know. I ate something last night and I don't feel very well.*
Farmacéutico	¿Tiene fiebre, diarrea o náuseas? ¿O es un dolor agudo?	*Do you have diarrhea or are you nauseous? Or is it a sharp pain?*
Karen	Es más bien un malestar general.	*I just don't feel well in general.*
Farmacéutico	¿Consultó a un médico?	*Did you see a doctor?*
Karen	Todavía no. ¿Necesito una receta?	*Not yet. Do I need a prescription?*
Farmacéutico	Para estas pastillas no, pero si usted se siente mal mañana, le aconsejo que vea a un médico.	*For these pills, no, but if you still feel ill tomorrow, I recommend you see a doctor.*
Karen	Primero voy a ver si estas pastillas me ayudan.	*First I'll see if these pills help me.*
Farmacéutico	Tome dos cada cuatro horas.	*Take two every four hours.*
Farmacéutico	Espero que se mejore.	*I hope you feel better.*

Action

	Spanish	English
Thomas	¿Tiene algo para el dolor de estómago?	*Do you have something for a stomachache?*
Farmacéutico	¿Qué le ocurre?	*What's wrong with you?*
Thomas	No lo sé. Comí algo anoche, y no me siento muy bien.	*I don't know. I ate something last night, and now I don't feel very well.*
Farmacéutico	¿Tiene diarrea o náuseas? ¿O es un dolor agudo?	*Do you have diarrhea or are you nauseous? Or is it a sharp pain?*
Thomas	Es más bien un malestar general.	*I just don't feel well in general.*
Farmacéutico	¿Consultó a un médico?	*Did you see a doctor?*
Thomas	Todavía no. ¿Necesito una receta?	*Not yet. Do I need a prescription?*
Farmacéutico	Para estas pastillas no, pero si usted se siente mal mañana, le aconsejo que vea a un médico.	*Not for these pills, but if you still feel sick tomorrow, I advise you to go to a doctor.*
Thomas	Primero voy a ver si estas pastillas me ayudan.	*First I'll see if these pills help me.*
Farmacéutico	Tome dos cada cuatro horas. Espero que se mejore.	*Take two every four hours. I hope you feel better.*

CHAPTER 14

Story

	Spanish	English
Médica	¿Hace cuánto tiempo que se siente mal?	How long have you been feeling ill?
Karen	Desde hace dos días.	For two days.
Médica	¿Le duele la cabeza? ¿Siente débil las piernas? ¿Siente vértigo?	Does your head hurt? Do you feel weak in the legs? Are you dizzy?
Karen	Sí, es un poco de todo. No sé qué me ocurre.	Yes, it's a little of everything. I don't know what's wrong with me.
Médica	Es posible que sea el efecto de la altitud. Es frecuente cuando uno no está acostumbrado.	It's possible that it's the effect of the altitude. It's common when one isn't used to it.
Karen	¿Y qué me recomienda usted?	And what do you recommend that I do?
Médica	Debe tener cuidado con las comidas y las bebidas.	You should be careful about food and drink.
Médica	Por ejemplo, evite las comidas pesadas con mucha grasa y también las bebidas alcohólicas.	For example, avoid heavy greasy foods and also alcoholic beverages.
Médica	Trate de descansar, y sobre todo, no se preocupe.	Try to rest, and above all, don't worry.
Karen	¿Necesito tomar alguna medicina especial?	Do I need to take any special medicine?
Médica	No, no es preciso. Se le pasará pronto.	No, it isn't necessary. It will go away soon.

Action

	Spanish	*English*
Médico	¿Hace cuánto tiempo que se siente mal?	*How long have you been feeling ill?*
Thomas	Desde hace dos días.	*For two days.*
Médico	¿Le duele la cabeza? ¿Siente débil las piernas? ¿Siente vértigo?	*Does your head hurt? Do you feel weak in the legs? Are you dizzy?*
Thomas	Sí, es un poco de todo. No sé qué me ocurre.	*Yes, it's a little of everything. I don't know what's wrong with me.*
Médico	Es posible que sea el efecto de la altitud. Es frecuente cuando uno no está acostumbrado.	*It's possible that it's the effect of the altitude. It's common when one isn't used to it.*
Thomas	¿Y qué me recomienda usted?	*And what do you recommend that I do?*
Médico	Debe tener cuidado con la comida y las bebidas.	*You should be careful about food and drink.*
Médico	Por ejemplo, evite las comidas pesadas con mucha grasa y también las bebidas alcohólicas.	*For example, avoid heavy greasy foods and also alcoholic beverages.*
Médico	Trate de descansar, y sobre todo, no se preocupe. Se le pasará pronto.	*Try to rest, and above all, don't worry. It will go away soon.*
Thomas	¿Necesito tomar alguna medicina especial?	*Do I need to take any special medicine?*
Médico	No, no es preciso.	*No, it isn't necessary.*

CHAPTER 15

Story

	Spanish	*English*
Empleada	Entonces, cuatro camisas, dos pantalones, un traje, seis pares de calcetines, cuatro calzoncillos y tres camisetas.	*Let's see, four shirts, two pairs of pants, a suit, six pairs of socks, four pairs of underwear, and three undershirts.*
Empleada	¿Para cuándo los quiere?	*When do you want them?*
Mario	Lo más pronto posible.	*As soon as possible.*
	También necesito que me ponga un botón en la camisa azul.	*I also need you to sew a button on the blue shirt.*
Mario	El ruedo del pantalón negro está suelto. ¿Puede arreglarmelo?	*The hem of the black pants is loose. Can you fix it?*
Empleada	¡Cómo no, señor!	*Of course, sir.*
Empleada	¿Quiere que le ponga almidón en las camisas y que le planche todo?	*Do you want me to put starch in the shirts and iron everything?*
Mario	Sí, está bien. Pero no ponga demasiado almidón en las camisas.	*Yes, fine. But don't put too much starch in the shirts.*
Empleada	Estará todo listo mañana por la tarde.	*Everything will be ready tomorrow afternoon.*
Mario	¿No puede ser por la mañana?	*Can't it be in the morning?*
Empleada	No puede ser antes porque tenemos muchos encargos acumulados.	*It can't be sooner than that because we have a lot of orders ahead of yours.*
Mario	De acuerdo. Hasta mañana.	*O.K. See you tomorrow.*

Action

	Spanish	*English*
Empleada	Entonces, cuatro camisas, dos pantalones, un traje, seis pares de calcetines, cuatro calzoncillos y tres camisetas.	*Let's see, four shirts, two pairs of pants, a suit, six pairs of socks, four pairs of underwear, and three undershirts.*
Empleada	¿Para cuándo los quiere?	*When do you want them?*
	Lo más pronto posible. También necesito que me ponga un botón en la camisa azul.	*As soon as possible. I also need you to sew a button on the blue shirt.*
Thomas	El ruedo del pantalón negro está suelto. ¿Puede arreglármelo?	*The hem of the black pants is loose. Can you fix it?*
Empleada	¡Cómo no, señor! ¿Quiere que le ponga almidón en las camisas y que le planche todo?	*Of course, sir. Do you want me to put starch in the shirts and iron everything?*
Thomas	Sí, está bien. Pero no ponga demasiado almidón en las camisas.	*Yes, fine. But don't put too much starch in the shirts.*
Empleada	Estará todo listo mañana por la tarde.	*Everything will be ready tomorrow afternoon.*
Thomas	¿No puede ser en la mañana?	*Can't it be in the morning?*
Empleada	No puede ser antes porque tenemos muchos encargos acumulados.	*It can't be sooner than that because we have a lot of orders ahead of yours.*
Thomas	De acuerdo. Hasta mañana.	*O.K. See you tomorrow.*

CHAPTER 16

Story

	Spanish	English
Mario	La verdad es que no me apetece manejar. Creo que es mejor tomar el autobús.	*The truth is I don't feel like driving. I think it's better to take a bus.*
Karen	¿Tú quieres ir con un tour organizado?	*Do you want to go on a tour?*
Mario	Sí, porque así no tendremos que preocupamos de nada.	*Yes, because then we won't have to worry about anything.*
Karen	Roberto me dijo que algunas de estas excurciones son muy interesantes.	*Roberto told me that some of these trips are really interesting.*
Mario	¿Adónde vamos? ¿Al mar o a las montañas?	*Where will we go? To the sea or to the mountains?*
Karen	Me dijeron que el viaje a Acapulco es muy agradable	*They told me that the trip to Acapulco is nice*
Karen	porque pasamos por Taxco, una ciudad colonial, y por las montañas también.	*because we go through Taxco, a colonial city, and through the mountains too.*
Mario	¿Vamos a quedarnos algunos días en la playa? A mi me gustaría ponerme moreno.	*Are we going to spend a few days at the beach? I'd like to get a tan.*
Karen	Sí, por supuesto.	*Yes, of course.*
Karen	También podemos recorrer la costa pata poder conocer algunos pueblos pequeños.	*We can also travel along the coast in order to see some of the small towns.*
Mario	De acuerdo.	*O.K.*
Mario	Mañana puedo ir a la agencia de viajes para decirles que queremos hacer un viaje a Acapulco.	*Tomorrow I can go to the travel agency and tell them we want to take a trip to Acapulco.*

CHAPTER 16

Action

	Spanish	English
Thomas	La verdad es que no me apetece manejar. Creo que es mejor tomar el autobús.	*The truth is I don't feel like driving. I think it's better to take a bus.*
Elena	¿Tú quieres ir con un tour organizado?	*Do you want to go on a tour?*
Thomas	Sí, porque así no tendremos que preocuparnos de nada.	*Yes, because then we won't have to worry about anything.*
Thomas	Roberto me dijo que algunas de estas excursiones son muy interesantes.	*Roberto told me that some of these trips are really interesting.*
Elena	¿Adónde vamos? ¿Al mar o a las montañas?	*Where will we go? To the sea or to the mountains?*
Thomas	Me dijeron que el viaje a Acapulco es agradable	*They told me that the trip to Acapulco is nice*
Thomas	porque pasamos por Taxco, una ciudad colonial, y las montañas también.	*because we go through Taxco, a colonial city, and through the mountains too.*
Elena	¿Vamos a quedarnos algunos días en la playa? A mí me gustaría ponerme morena.	*Are we going to spend a few days at the beach? I'd like to get a tan.*
Thomas	Sí, por supuesto. También podemos recorrer la costa para poder conocer algunos pueblos pequeños.	*Yes, of course. We can also travel along the coast in order to see some of the small towns.*

CHAPTER 17

Story

	Spanish	*English*
Mario	Buenos días. Mi familia y yo queremos ir de vacaciones a Acapulco con un tour.	*Good morning. My family and I want to go on an organized tour to Acapulco for vacation.*
Mario	¿Puede darme información sobre los viajes?	*Can you give me some information about the trip?*
Agente	Sí, señor. Tenemos varias clases de excursiones. ¿Quieren ir en primera clase?	*Yes, Sir. We have several different kinds of tours. Do you want to go first class?*
Mario	Sí, y quiero reservar cuatro plazas.	*Yes, and I want to reserve four places.*
Agente	¿Cuándo quieren viajar?	*When do you want to travel?*
Mario	Tenemos una semana libre, a partir del viernes próximo.	*We have a week free, starting next Friday.*
Agente	Bueno. Pueden salir ustedes el sábado pr la mañana y llegar a Taxco por la noche.	*Fine. You can leave on Saturday morning and get to Taxco that night.*
Agente	La excursión incluye alojamiento en Taxco, cena y desayuno,	*The tour includes hotel accommodations in Taxco, dinner and breakfast,*
Agente	y por la noche pueden asistir a una representación folklórica.	*and in the evening you can attend a floor show of folkloric dances.*
Mario	Me parece estupendo.	*It sounds great to me.*
Mario	¿Habrá tiempo para visitar las tiendas?	*Will there be time to visit the stores?*
Agente	Sí, tendrán un par de horas antes de salir para Acapulco.	*Yes, you'll have a couple of hours before you leave for Acapulco.*

CHAPTER 17

Action

	Spanish	*English*
Elena	Buenos días. Mi familia y yo queremos ir de vacaciones a Acapulco con un tour.	*Good morning. My family and I want to go on an organized tour to Acapulco for vacation.*
Elena	¿Puede darme información sobre los viajes?	*Can you give me some information about the trips?*
Agente	Sí, señora. TenemSpanishos varias clases de excursiones. ¿Quieren ir en primera clase?	*Yes, Ma'am. We have several different kinds of tours. Do you want to go first class?*
Elena	Sí, y quiero reservar cuatro plazas. Tenemos una semana libre, a partir del viernes próximo.	*Yes, and I want to reserve four places. We have a week free, starting next Friday.*
Agente	Bueno. Pueden salir ustedes el sábado por la mañana y llegar a Taxco por la noche.	*Fine. You can leave on Saturday morning and get to Taxco that night.*
Agente	La excursión incluye alojamiento en Taxco, cena y desayuno,	*The tour includes hotel accommodations in Taxco, dinner and breakfast,*
Agente	y por la noche pueden asistir a una representación folklórica.	*and in the evening you can attend a floor show of folkloric dances.*
Elena	Me parece estupendo. ¿Habrá tiempo para visitar las tiendas?	*It sounds great to me. Will there be time to visit the stores?*
Agente	Sí, tendrán un par de horas antes de salir para Acapulco.	*Yes, you'll have a couple of hours before you leave for Acapulco.*

CHAPTER 18

Story

	Spanish	English
Mario	¿Dónde está la carne en este restaurante?	*Don't they have any meat in this restaurant?*
Karen	¿Pero no querías comer pescado?	*But didn't you want to eat seafood?*
Mario	Quería, pero ahora quiero comer carne.	*I did want to, but now I want to eat meat.*
Karen	Pues vas a tener que preguntarle al camarero.	*Well you'll have to ask the waiter.*
Mario	¿Es posible comer un bistec con papas fritas? Es que no me apetece comer pescado hoy.	*Is it possible to get a steak and fried potatoes? I just don't feel like eating fish today.*
Camarero	Por supuesto. Hablaré con el cocinero.	*Of course. I'll talk to the chef.*
Camarero	Y la señora y los niños, ¿qué van a tomar?	*And the lady and the children, what will they have to eat?*
Karen	¿Tienen alguna especialidad?	*Do you have any specialities of the house?*
Camarero	Sí, camarones, langosta y atún.	*Yes, shrimp, lobster and tuna.*
Karen	La langosta para mí.	*Lobster for me.*
Karen	Los niños son como su padre. Prefieren la carne.	*The children are like their father. They prefer meat.*
Camarero	¿Algo de beber?	*Anything to drink?*
Mario	Vino para nosotros y jugo para los niños.	*Wine for us, and juice for the children.*

Action

	Spanish	English
Thomas	¿Dónde está la carne en este restaurante?	*Don't they have any meat in this restaurant?*
Elena	¿Pero no querías comer pescado?	*But didn't you want to eat seafood?*
Thomas	Quería, pero ahora quiero comer carne.	*I did want to, but now I want to eat meat.*
Elena	Pues vas a tener que preguntarle al camarero.	*Well you'll have to ask the waiter.*
Thomas	¿Es posible comer un bistec con papas fritas? Es que no me apetece comer pescado hoy.	*Is it possible to get a steak and fried potatoes? I just don't feel like eating fish today.*
Camarero	Por supuesto. Hablaré con el cocinero. Y la señora y los niños, ¿qué van a tomar?	*Of course. I'll talk to the chef. And the lady and the children, what will they have to eat?*
Elena	¿Tienen alguna especialidad?	*Do you have any specialities of the house?*
Camarero	Sí, camarones, langosta y atún.	*Yes, shrimp, lobster and tuna.*
Elena	La langosta para mí. Los niños son como su padre. Prefieren la carne.	*Lobster for me. And the children are like their father. They prefer meat.*
Camarero	¿Algo de beber?	*Anything to drink?*
Thomas	Vino para nosotros y jugo para los niños.	*Wine for us, and juice for the children.*

CHAPTER 19

Story

	Spanish	English
Karen	¿Qué te parece este pañuelo para Silvia?	*What do you think about this scarf for Silvia?*
Mario	Creo que los colores son muy chillones.	*I think the colors are too loud.*
Mario	¿No quieres buscar algo más discreto?	*Don't you want to look for something more subtle?*
Karen	Tienes razón. Creo que aquel azul es más discreto.	*You're right. I think that blue one over there is more elegant.*
Mario	¿Qué podemos comprarle a Roberto?	*What can we buy for Roberto?*
Karen	A Roberto le encanta la música clásica. Cómprale un disco.	*Roberto loves classical music. Buy him a record.*
Mario	Tenemos que comprarles unos juguetes a los niños también.	*We have to buy some toys for the children too.*
Mario	Voy a preguntar a la dependienta dónde está la sección de juguetes.	*I'm going to ask the saleswoman where the toy section is.*
Karen	No te olvides del libro para Eduardo.	*Don't forget the book for Eduardo.*
Karen	Tienen una buena seleccón ahí, junto a la caja.	*They have a good selection there, next to the cash register.*
Mario	No, prefiero ir a la librería. Allá los libros son más baratos que aquí.	*No, I prefer to go to the bookstore. Besides, the books are cheaper than here.*

Action

	Spanish	English
Elena	¿Qué te parece este pañuelo para Silvia?	*What do you think about this scarf for Silvia?*
Thomas	Creo que los colores son muy chillones. ¿No quieres buscar algo más discreto?	*I think the colors are too loud. Don't you want to look for something more subtle?*
Elena	Tienes razón. Creo que aquel azul es más elegante.	*You're right. I think that blue one over there is more elegant.*
Thomas	¿Qué podemos comprarle a Roberto?	*And what can we buy for Roberto?*
Elena	A Roberto le encanta la música clásica. Cómprale un disco.	*Roberto loves classical music. Buy him a record.*
Thomas	Tenemos que comprarles unos juguetes a los niños, también.	*We have to buy some toys for the children too.*
Thomas	Voy a preguntar a la dependienta dónde está la sección de juguetes.	*I'm going to ask the saleswoman where the toy section is.*
Elena	No te olvides del libro para Eduardo. Tienen una buena selección ahí, junto a la caja.	*Don't forget the book for Eduardo. They have a good selection there, next to the cash register.*
Thomas	No, prefiero ir a la librería. Allá los libros son más baratos que aquí.	*No, I prefer to go to the bookstore. Besides, the books are cheaper than here.*

CHAPTER 20

Story

	Spanish	English
Mario	Estoy buscando una casa o un apartamento para cuatro personas. Somos un matrimonio y dos hijos.	*I'm looking for a house or an apartment for four persons. We're a married couple and two children.*
Agente	¿Desea una casa dentro de la ciudad o en las afueras?	*Do you want a house in the city or in the suburbs?*
Agente	Fuera de la ciudad tiene usted la ventaja del precio y del espacio.	*Outside the city you have the advantage of better prices and more space.*
Mario	No, a mi esposa no le gusta vivir en el campo porque le lleva mucho tiempo llegar al trabajo.	*No, my wife doesn't like to live in the country because it takes her too long to get to work.*
Agente	Podemos ofrecerle una casa cerca el centro con seis dormitorios, cocina, comedor,	*We can offer you a house near the downtown area with six bedrooms, kitchen and dining room,*
Agente	dos cuartos de baño y una sala de estar.	*two bathrooms, and a living room.*
Agente	También tiene un garaje de dos plazas y un patio. Pero no está amueblada.	*It also has a two car garage and a patio. But it isn't furnished.*
Mario	No, es que vamos a estar aquí sólo un año. Necesitamos una vivienda amueblada.	*No, we're only going to be here for a year. We need a place that's furnished.*

Action

	Spanish	English
Thomas	Estoy buscando una casa o un apartamento para cuatro personas. Somos un matrimonio y dos hijos.	*I'm looking for a house or an apartment for four persons. We're a married couple and two children.*
Agente	¿Desea una casa dentro de la ciudad o en las afueras?	*Do you want a house in the city or in the suburbs?*
Agente	Fuera de la ciudad tiene usted la ventaja del precio y del espacio.	*Outside the city you have the advantage of better prices and more space.*
Thomas	No, porque me lleva mucho tiempo llegar al trabajo. Y a mi esposa no le gusta vivir en el campo.	*No, because it would take me too long to get to work. And my wife doesn't like to live in the country.*
Agente	Podemos ofrecerle una casa cerca del centro con seis dormitorios, cocina y comedor,	*We can offer you a house near the downtown area with six bedrooms, kitchen and dining room,*
Agente	dos cuartos de baño y una sala de estar.	*two bathrooms, and a living room.*
Agente	También tiene un garaje de dos plazas y un patio. Pero no está amueblada.	*It also has a two car garage and a patio. But it isn't furnished.*
Thomas	No, es que vamos a estar aquí sólo un año. Necesitamos una vivienda amueblada.	*No, we're only going to be here for a year. We need a place that's furnished.*

CHAPTER 21

Story

	Spanish	English
Karen	Necesito comprar carne, pescado, verduras, huevos, leche y fruta.	*I need to buy meat, fish, vegetables, eggs, milk and fruit.*
Silvia	Bueno, mira, en este mercado puedes compara lo que quieras.	*Fine, look, in this market you can buy whatever you want.*
Silvia	En esta parte tienes la carne de cerdo y de res. El pescado está un poco más lejos, a la derecha.	*In this part, you can have the pork and beef. The fish is a little further ahead, on the right.*
Silvia	Y a continuación, podemos comprar la fruta y las verduras.	*And farther on, we can buy fruit and vegetables.*
Karen	¿Es más barato comprar aquí u en el supermercado?	*Is it cheaper to shop here or at the supermarket?*
Silvia	Normalmente, aquí es más barato,	*Normally it's cheaper here,*
Silvia	y los productos son más frescos, sobre todo las verduras.	*and the products are fresher, especially the vegetables.*
Karen	También necesito comprar harina.	*I also need to buy flour.*
Silvia	La harina tienes que comprarla en el supermercado. Aquí no la tienen.	*You have to buy flour at the supermarket. They don't have it here.*
Karen	Bueno, vamos a empezar por la carnicería.	*O.K. Let's start at the meat counter.*

Action

	Spanish	English
Elena	Necesito comprar carne, pescado, verduras, huevos, leche y fruta.	*I need to buy meat, fish, vegetables, eggs, milk and fruit.*
Silvia	Bueno, mira, en este mercado puedes comprar lo que quieras.	*Fine, look, in this market you can buy whatever you want.*
Silvia	En esta parte tienes la carne de cerdo y de res. El pescado está un poco más lejos, a la derecha.	*In this part, you can have the pork and beef. The fish is a little further ahead, on the right.*
Silvia	Y a continuación, podemos comprar la fruta y las verduras.	*And farther on, we can buy fruit and vegetables.*
Elena	¿Es más barato comprar aquí o en el supermercado?	*Is it cheaper to shop here or at the supermarket?*
Silvia	Normalmente, aquí es más barato, y los productos son más frescos, sobre todo las verduras.	*Normally it's cheaper here, and the products are fresher, especially the vegetables.*
Elena	También necesito comprar harina.	*I also need to buy flour.*
Silvia	La harina tienes que comprarla en el supermercado. Aquí no la tienen.	*You have to buy flour at the supermarket. They don't have it here.*
Elena	Bueno, vamos a empezar por la carnicería.	*O.K. Let's start at the meat counter.*

CHAPTER 22

Story

	Spanish	*English*
Karen	Deme dos kilos de chuletas de cerdo, uno de ternera y uno de salchichas.	*Give me two kilos of pork chops, one of veal, and one of sausages.*
Carnicero	¿Algo más?	*Anything else?*
Karen	No, gracias. ¿Puede envolverlo todo y meterlo en una bolsa de plástico?	*No, thanks. Can you wrap it all up and put it in a plastic bag?*
Carnicero	¡Cómo no! Aquí tiene.	*Of course. Here you are.*
Karen	Quiero medio kilo de limones, cuatro de naranjas, dos de bananas y una sandia.	*I want half a kilo of lemons, four of oranges, two of bananas and a watermelon.*
Frutera	La sandia pesa más de cinco kilos.	*The watermelon weighs over five kilos.*
Frutera	¿Quiere usted una más pequeña?	*Do you want a smaller one?*
Karen	No, ésa está bien.	*No, that one is fine.*
Silvia	Si sigues comprando tanto, vas a necesitar una empleada para ayudarte con las compras.	*If you keep buying so much, you're going to need a maid to help you do the shopping*

Action

	Spanish	*English*
Elena	Deme dos kilos de chuletas de cerdo, uno de ternera y uno de salchichas.	*Give me two kilos of pork chops, one of veal, and one of sausages.*
Carnicero	¿Algo más?	*Anything else?*
Elena	No, gracias. ¿Puede envolverlo todo y meterlo en una bolsa de plástico?	*No, thanks. Can you wrap it all up and put it in a plastic bag?*
Carnicero	¡Cómo no! Aquí tiene.	*Of course. Here you are.*
Elena	Quiero medio kilo de limones, cuatro de naranjas, dos de bananas y una sandía.	*I want half a kilo of lemons, four of oranges, two of bananas and a watermelon.*
Frutero	La sandía pesa más de cinco kilos. ¿Quiere usted una más pequeña?	*The watermelon weighs over five kilos. Do you want a smaller one?*
Elena	No, ésa está bien.	*No, that one is fine.*
Silvia	Si sigues comprando tanto, vas a necesitar a una empleada para ayudarte con las compras.	*If you keep buying so much, you're going to need a maid to help you do the shopping*

CHAPTER 23

Story

	Spanish	*English*
Karen	Lupe, no te olvides de cambiar las sábanas hoy antes de hacer las camas.	*Lupe, don't forget to change the sheets today before you make the beds.*
Lupe	¿Paso primero la aspiradora en la sala?	*Should I run the vacuum cleaner in the living room first?*
Karen	No, arregla primero los dormitorios y barre después el pasillo. Deja la sala para el final.	*No, first straighten up the bedrooms and then sweep the hallway. Leave the living room for last.*
Lupe	¿Cuándo quiere que lave la ropa?	*When do you want me to wash the clothes?*
Karen	La lavadora no funciona. Voy a llamar esta tarde a un técnico para que arregle el aparato.	*The washing machine isn't working. I'm going to call this afternoon a repairman to come and fix the machine.*
Karen	Lleva la ropa a la lavandería cuando vayas a hacer las compras.	*Take the clothes to the laundry when you go to do the shopping.*
Lupe	¿Quiere que limpie las ventanas también?	*Do you want me to wash the windows too?*
Karen	Bueno, si tienes tiempo hoy, limpia las ventanas y quita el polvo a los muebles.	*Sure, if you have time today, wash the windows and dust the furniture.*
Lupe	A ver cuánto tardo en el mercado.	*I'll see how long it takes me at the market.*

Action

	Spanish	*English*
Elena	Lupe, no te olvides de cambiar las sábanas hoy antes de hacer las camas.	*Lupe, don't forget to change the sheets today before you make the beds.*
Lupe	¿Paso primero la aspiradora en la sala?	*Should I run the vacuum cleaner in the living room first?*
Elena	No, arregla primero los dormitorios y barre después el pasillo. Deja la sala para el final.	*No, first straighten up the bedrooms and then sweep the hallway. Leave the living room for last.*
Lupe	¿Cuándo quiere que lave la ropa?	*When do you want me to wash the clothes?*
Elena	La lavadora no funciona. Lleva la ropa a la lavandería cuando vayas a hacer las compras.	*The washing machine isn't working. Take the clothes to the laundry when you go to do the shopping.*
Elena	Voy a llamar esta tarde a un técnico para que arregle el aparato.	*I'm going to call this afternoon a repairman to come and fix the machine.*
Lupe	¿Quiere que limpie las ventanas también?	*Do you want me to wash the windows too?*
Elena	Bueno, si tienes tiempo hoy, limpia las ventanas y quita el polvo a los muebles.	*Sure, if you have time today, wash the windows and dust the furniture.*
Lupe	A ver cuánto tardo en el mercado.	*I'll see how long it takes me at the market.*

CHAPTER 24

Story

	Spanish	*English*
Mario	¿Encontraste el vestido que buscabas?	*Did you find the dress that you were looking for?*
Karen	No. Había uno negro que me gustaba mucho pero la talla era demasiado grande para mí.	*No, there was a black one that I liked a lot but the size was too large for me.*
Mario	¿No tenían tallas más pequeñas?	*Didn't they have smaller sizes?*
Karen	Sí, pero no en negro. Había uno amarillo horroroso.	*Yes, but not in black. There was a yellow one that was horrible.*
Karen	Encontré una bluse muy linda que hace juego con mi falda gris.	*I found a very pretty blouse that matches my gray skirt.*
Karen	¿Y tú, compraste los zapatos?	*And you, did you buy some shoes?*
Mario	Sí. Encontré unos zapatos de cuero a muy buen precio.	*Yes. I found some leather shoes at a very good price.*
Mario	También compré un traje nuevo.	*I also bought a new suit.*
Karen	¿Otro traje? ¡Tienes ya tantos!	*Another suit? You already have so many!*
Mario	Sólo tengo tres y todos viejos.	*I only have three and they're all old.*
Mario	Lo que necesito ahora son camisas.	*What I need now are shirts.*
Karen	Yo iré contigo a comprarlas.	*I'll go with you to buy them.*
Karen	No siempre tienes buen gusto, ¿sabes?	*You don't always have the best of taste, you know.*
Mario	De paso me aconsejas con los pantalones.	*You can give me some advice about the pants, then, while you're at it.*

CHAPTER 24

Story

	Spanish	English
Thomas	¿Encontraste el vestido que buscabas?	*Did you find the dress that you were looking for?*
Elena	No. Había uno negro que me gustaba mucho pero la talla era demasiado grande para mí.	*No, there was a black one that I liked a lot but the size was too large for me.*
Thomas	¿No tenían tallas más pequeñas?	*Didn't they have smaller sizes?*
Elena	Sí, pero no en negro. Había uno amarillo horroroso.	*Yes, but not in black. There was a yellow one that was horrible.*
Elena	Encontré una blusa muy linda que hace juego con mi falda gris. ¿Y tú, compraste los zapatos?	*I found a very pretty blouse that matches my gray skirt. And you, did you buy some shoes?*
Thomas	Sí. Encontré unos zapatos de cuero a muy buen precio. También compré un traje nuevo.	*Yes. I found some leather shoes at a very good price. I also bought a new suit.*
Elena	¿Otro traje? ¡Tienes ya tantos!	*Another suit? You already have so many!*
Thomas	Sólo tengo tres y todos viejos. Lo que necesito ahora son camisas.	*I only have three and they're all old. What I need now are shirts.*
Elena	Yo iré contigo a comprarlas. No siempre tienes buen gusto, ¿sabes?	*I'll go with you to buy them. You don't always have the best of taste, you know.*
Thomas	De paso me aconsejas con los pantalones.	*You can give me some advice about the pants, then, while you're at it.*

CHAPTER 25

Story

	Spanish	English
Karen	¿Ha llegado una transferencia desde Estados Unidos a nombre de Karen Santiago?	*Has some money arrived from the United States in the name of Karen Santiago?*
Empleado	¿Tiene usted una cuenta aquí?	*Do you have an account here?*
Karen	Sí, abrí una cuenta hace un mes.	*Yes, I opened an account a month ago.*
Empleado	¿Cuál es el número?	*What is the number?*
Karen	Lo tengo aquí. Es el C-4400761.	*I have it here. It's C-4400761.*
Empleado	Espere un momento. Sí, en efecto. Tiene usted una cuenta con un balance de veinte mil pesos.	*Wait a minute. Yes, that's right. You have an account with a balance of twenty thousand pesos.*
Karen	Estupendo. Quiero encargar unos cheques de viaje. Cinco mil pesos, pero en sucres, de ser posible.	*Great. I want to get some traveler's checks. Five thousand pesos, but in sucres, if that's possible.*
Empleado	Estarán mañana por la mañana a última hora.	*They'll be ready late tomorrow morning.*
Empleado	¿Desea algo más?	*Do you want anything else?*
Karen	No, es todo, gracias. Hasta luego.	*No, that's all, thanks. See you later.*

Action

	Spanish	English
Thomas	¿Ha llegado una transferencia desde Estados Unidos a nombre de Thomas Smith?	*Has some money arrived from the United States in the name of Thomas Smith?*
Empleado	¿Tiene usted una cuenta aquí?	*Do you have an account here?*
Thomas	Sí, abrí una cuenta hace un mes.	*Yes, I opened an account a month ago.*
Empleado	¿Cuál es el número?	*What is the number?*
Thomas	Lo tengo aquí. Es el C-4400761.	*I have it here. It's C-4400761.*
Empleado	Espere un momento. Sí, en efecto. Tiene usted una cuenta con un balance de veinte mil pesos.	*Wait a minute. Yes, that's right. You have an account with a balance of twenty thousand pesos.*
Thomas	Estupendo. Quiero encargar unos cheques de viaje. Cinco mil pesos, pero en sucres, de ser posible.	*Great. I want to get some traveler's checks. Five thousand pesos, but in sucres, if that's possible.*
Empleado	Estarán mañana por la mañana a última hora. ¿Desea algo más?	*They'll be ready late tomorrow morning. Do you want anything else?*
Thomas	No, es todo, gracias. Hasta luego.	*No, that's all, thanks. See you later.*

CHAPTER 26

Story

	Spanish	English
Karen	Lléneme el tanque con super, por favor.	*Fill the tank with super, please.*
Empleado	Sí señora.	*Yes, ma'am.*
Empleado	Me parece que tiene una llanta desinflada. ¿Quiere que le ponga aire?	*I think you have a flat tire. Do you want me to put some air in it?*
Karen	Ah, sí, por favor. ¿Puede revisarme también el aceite y el agua?	*Oh, yes, please. Can you also check the oil and the water for me?*
Empleado	Ahora mismo. Todo está bien, pero le puse un poco de aceite.	*Right away. Everything's fine, but I put in a little oil.*
Karen	Bien. ¿Puedo pagar con tarjeta de crédito?	*Good. Can I pay with a credit card?*
Empleado	No señora. Tiene usted que pagar en efectivo. No aceptamos tarjetas.	*No, ma'am. You have to pay cash. We don't take credit cards.*
Karen	No sé si va a alcanzarme.	*I don't know if I have enough.*
Karen	¿Cuánto es?	*How much it is?*
Empleado	Treinta pesos.	*Thirty pesos.*
Karen	Ah, pues sí, mire. Tengo justo esa cantidad. Aquí tiene.	*Oh, yes, look. I have just that amount. Here you are.*
Empleado	Espere a que le limpie el parabrisas.	*Wait until I clean your windshield.*

Action

	Spanish	English
Elena	Lléneme el tanque con super, por favor.	*Fill the tank with super, please.*
Empleado	Sí, señora. Me parece que tiene una llanta desinflada. ¿Quiere que le ponga aire?	*Yes, ma'am. I think you have a flat tire. Do you want me to put some air in it?*
Elena	Ah, sí, por favor. ¿Puede revisarme también el aceite y el agua?	*Oh, yes, please. Can you also check the oil and the water for me?*
Empleado	Ahora mismo. Todo está bien, pero le puse un poco de aceite.	*Right away. Everything's fine, but I put in a little oil.*
Elena	Bien. ¿Puedo pagar con tarjeta de crédito?	*Good. Can I pay with a credit card?*
Empleado	No señora. Tiene usted que pagar en efectivo. No aceptamos tarjetas.	*No, ma'am. You have to pay cash. We don't take credit cards.*
Elena	No sé si va a alcanzarme. ¿Cuánto es?	*I don't know if I have enough. How much it is?*
Empleado	Treinta pesos.	*Thirty pesos.*
Elena	Ah, pues sí, mire. Tengo justo esa cantidad. Aquí tiene.	*Oh, yes, look. I have just that amount. Here you are.*
Empleado	Espere a que le limpie el parabrisas.	*Wait until I clean your windshield.*

CHAPTER 27

Story

	Spanish	English
Karen	Hemos recibido una carta de tus padres hoy. Dicen que estuvieron en Florida con tu hermano.	*We got a letter from your parents today. They said they were in Florida with your brother.*
Mario	¿Y qué más?	*And what else?*
Karen	Están pensando en venir de vacaciones para Navidad, pero tu mamá no sabe si tendrá muchos días libres.	*They're thinking about coming for a vacation at Christmas, but your mom doesn't know if she'll have many days free.*
Mario	¡Qué raro! Ella ya no trabaja.	*How strange! She doesn't work any more.*
Karen	No, pero tu cuñada quiere pasar unos días con ellos en esas fechas. Sabes que les gusta ver a sus nietos.	*No, but your sister in law wants to spend a few days with them then. You know how much they like to see their grandchildren.*
Mario	¡Pues aquí tienen dos nietos también!	*Well they have two grandchildren here too!*
Karen	No es para tomarlo a mal.	*Don't take it the wrong way.*
Karen	Pueden venir en Semana Santa. Hace mejor tiempo y también es el cumpleaños del pequeño.	*They can come here for Easter week. The weather's better, and it's also the baby's birthday.*
Mario	Como tú quieras.	*Have it your way.*

Action

	Spanish	English
Elena	Hemos recibido carta de tus padres hoy. Dicen que estuvieron en Florida con tu hermano.	*We got a letter from your parents today. They said they were in Florida with your brother.*
Thomas	¿Y qué más?	*And what else?*
Elena	Están pensando en venir de vacaciones para Navidad, pero tu mamá no sabe si tendrá muchos días libres.	*They're thinking about coming for a vacation at Christmas, but your mom doesn't know if she'll have many days free.*
Thomas	¡Qué raro! Ella ya no trabaja.	*How strange! She doesn't work any more.*
Elena	No, pero tu cuñada quiere pasar unos días con ellos en esas fechas. Sabes que les gusta ver a sus nietos.	*No, but your sister in law wants to spend a few days with them then. You know how much they like to see their grandchildren.*
Thomas	¡Pues aquí tienen dos nietos también!	*Well they have two grandchildren here too!*
Elena	No es para tomarlo a mal. Pueden venir en Semana Santa.	*Don't take it the wrong way. They can come here for Easter week.*
Elena	Hace mejor tiempo y también es el cumpleaños del pequeño.	*The weather's better, and it's also the baby's birthday.*
Thomas	Como tú quieras.	*Have it your way.*

CHAPTER 28

Story

	Spanish	English
Karen	Quería cortarme el pelo, pero no mucho. Sólo las puntas. El flequillo déjelo como está.	*I wanted to cut my hair, but not very much. Just the ends. Leave the bangs the way they are.*
Peluquera	¿Quiere lavarse el pelo antes?	*Do you want a shampoo first?*
Karen	Sí, pero tengo el pelo muy seco. ¿Puede ponerme un buen acondicionador?	*Yes, but my hair's very dry. Can you put a good conditioner on it?*
Peluquera	¡Cómo no!	*Of course!*
Peluquera	¿No piensa usted hacerse una permanente? Le quedaría muy bien.	*Of course! You're not thinking about getting a permanent? It would look good on you.*
Karen	Sí, ya lo he pensado.	*Yes, I've thought about it.*
Karen	Lo que pasa es que a mi marido no le gustan los rizos.	*The problem is that my husband doesn't like curls.*
Peluquera	No, es que le daría un poso más de volúmen.	*No, it would just give you a little more body.*
Karen	Eso le vendría bien a mi marido porque se está quedando casi calvo.	*That's what my husband needs, because he's practically going bald.*
Peluquera	El problema con los hombres es que no se cuidan mucho.	*The problem with men is that they don't take good care of themselves.*

Action

	Spanish	English
Elena	Quería cortarme el pelo, pero no mucho. Sólo las puntas. El flequillo déjelo como está.	*I wanted to cut my hair, but not very much. Just the ends. Leave the bangs the way they are.*
Peluquera	¿Quiere lavarse el pelo antes?	*Do you want a shampoo first?*
Elena	Sí, pero tengo el pelo muy seco. ¿Puede ponerme un buen acondicionador?	*Yes, but my hair's very dry. Can you put a good conditioner on it?*
Peluquera	¡Cómo no! ¿No piensa usted hacerse el permanente? Le quedaría muy bien.	*Of course! You're not thinking about getting a permanent? It would look good on you.*
Elena	Sí, ya lo he pensado. Lo que pasa es que a mi marido no le gustan los rizos.	*Yes, I've thought about it. The problem is that my husband doesn't like curls.*
Peluquera	No, es que le daría un poco más de volumen.	*No, it would just give you a little more body.*
Elena	Eso le vendría bien a mi marido porque se está quedando casi calvo.	*That's what my husband needs, because he's practically going bald.*
Peluquera	El problema con los hombres es que no se cuidan mucho.	*The problem with men is that they don't take good care of themselves.*

CHAPTER 29

Story

	Spanish	*English*
Karen	¿Tiene usted algún plan para el viernes en la noche?	*Do you have plans for Friday night?*
Directora	No. Espero que terminemos el trabajo y así tendré dos días para ver la ciudad.	*No. I hope that we'll finish the job and then I'll have two days to see the city.*
Karen	Hay una representación de teatro en Bellas Artes y pensé que quizás le gustaría acompañarnos.	*There's a play at the Bellas Artes theater and I thought that perhaps you'd like to accompany us.*
Directora	¿No es un poco tarde para conseguir boletos?	*Isn't it a little late to get tickets?*
Karen	No, no se preocupe. Estoy segura que quedan entradas.	*No, don't worry. I'm sure there are tickets left.*
Directora	Por cierto, ¿a qué hora es la función?	*By the way, at what time is the performance?*
Karen	Es a las nueve. Pero vamos a cenar en un restaurante antes.	*At nine. But we're going to have dinner in a restaurant beforehand.*
Directora	Ah, Eduardo ya me invitó a cenar en su casa.	*Ah, Eduardo already invited me to have dinner at his house.*
Karen	¡Qué lástima! Quizás en otra ocasión, entonces.	*What a shame! Maybe some other time, then.*
Directora	Pero sí me gustaría acompañarles al teatro.	*But I would like to join you at the theater.*
Directora	¿Podría usted pasar a recogerme en mi hotel a las ocho?	*Fine. Can you come to pick me up at my hotel at eight?*
Karen	No hay ningún problema.	*No problem.*

Action

	Spanish	*English*
Thomas	¿Tiene usted algún plan para el viernes en la noche?	*Do you have plans for Friday night?*
Directora	No. Espero que terminemos el trabajo y así tendré dos días para ver la ciudad.	*No. I hope that we'll finish the job and then I'll have two days to see the city.*
Thomas	Hay una representación de teatro en Bellas Artes y pensé que quizás le gustaría acompañarnos.	*There's a play at the Bellas Artes theater and I thought that perhaps you'd like to accompany us.*
Directora	¿No es un poco tarde para conseguir boletos?	*Isn't it a little late to get tickets?*
Thomas	No, no se preocupe. Estoy seguro que quedan entradas.	*No, don't worry. I'm sure there are tickets left.*
Directora	Por cierto, ¿a qué hora es la función?	*By the way, at what time is the performance?*
Thomas	A las nueve.	*At nine.*
Directora	Muy bien. ¿Podría usted pasar a recogerme en mi hotel a las ocho?	*Fine. Can you come to pick me up at my hotel at eight?*
Thomas	No hay ningún problema.	*No problem.*

CHAPTER 30

Story

	Spanish	English
Karen	¿Hay demora con el vuelo para Chicago?	*Is there a delay on the flight to Chicago.?*
Empleado	No. Saldrá a las 11:45 desde la puerta 16.	*No. It'll leave at 11:45, from gate 16.*
Empleado	¿Quieren documentar el equipaje ahora?	*Do you want to check your baggage now?*
Mario	Sí. llevamos muchas maletas.	*Yes. We're carrying a lot of luggage.*
Empleado	¿Tiene los pasajes?	*Do you have your tickets?*
Karen	Sí, claro. Aquí tiene.	*Yes, of course. Here they are.*
Empleado	Gracias. Pidieron asientos en la sección de no fumar, ¿verdad?	*Thank you. You asked for seats in the no smoking section, right?*
Karen	Sí.	*Yes.*
Mario	¿Con cuánto tiempo de antelación tenemos que estar aquí?	*How far in advance do we need to be here?*
Empleado	Veinte minutos antes del embarque. Anunciarán la salida en la sala de espera.	*Twenty minutes before boarding. They'll announce the departure in the waiting room.*
Karen	No puedo creer que es hora de salir, Mario.	*I can't believe that it's time to leave, Mario.*
Karen	Después de pasar un año tan agradable en México, hay que regresar a Chicago.	*After spending a very enjoyable year here in Mexico, it's necessary to return to Chicago.*
Mario	Tampoco lo creo. Pero si no me equivoco, tenemos tres semanas libres en julio,	*I don't believe it either. But, if I'm not mistaken, we have three weeks off in July,*
Mario	y si economizamos un poco, ¡podremos venir a México de vacaciones!	*and if we save a little, we'll be able to return to Mexico on vacation!*

CHAPTER 30

Action

	Spanish	*English*
Thomas	¿Hay demora con el vuelo para Chicago?	*Is there a delay on the flight to Chicago.?*
Empleado	No. Saldrá a las 11:45 desde la puerta 16. ¿Quieren documentar el equipaje ahora?	*No. It'll leave at 11:45, from gate 16. Do you want to check your baggage now?*
Thomas	Sí. Llevamos muchas maletas.	*Yes. We're carrying a lot of luggage.*
Empleado	¿Tiene los pasajes?	*Do you have your tickets?*
Elena	Sí, claro. Aquí tiene.	*Yes, of course. Here they are.*
Empleado	Gracias. Pidieron asientos en la sección de no fumar, ¿verdad?	*Thank you. You asked for seats in the no smoking section, right?*
Elena	Sí. ¿Con cuánto tiempo de antelación tenemos que estar aquí?	*Yes. How far in advance do we need to be here?*
Empleado	Veinte minutos antes del embarque. Anunciarán la salida en la sala de espera.	*Twenty minutes before boarding. They'll announce the departure in the waiting room.*
Elena	No puedo creer que es hora de salir, Thomas.	*I can't believe that it's time to leave, Thomas.*
Elena	Después de pasar un año tan agradable aquí en México, hay que regresar a Chicago.	*After spending a very enjoyable year here in Mexico, it's necessary to return to Chicago.*
Thomas	Tampoco lo creo. Pero, si no me equivoco, tengo tres semanas libres en julio,	*I don't believe it either. But, if I'm not mistaken, I have three weeks off in July,*
Thomas	y si economizamos un poco, ¡podremos venir a México de vacaciones!	*and if we save a little, we'll be able to return to Mexico on vacation!*

Learn To Speak Vocabulary

Spanish	English
a continuación	*further on*
a la derecha	*to, on the right*
a la derecha de	*to the right of*
a la izquierda	*to, on the left*
a la izquierda de	*to the left of*
a la vuelta	*around the corner*
a partir de	*starting on*
¿a qué hora?	*what time? at what time?*
a veces	*sometimes*
abierto	*open*
el abogado	*lawyer*
abrazar	*to embrace*
abril	*April*
abrir	*to open*
la abuela	*grandmother*
el abuelo	*grandfather*
el aburrimiento	*boredom*
el aceite	*oil*
aceptar	*accept*
acompañar	*to go with, accompany*
el acondicionador	*conditioner*
aconsejar	*to advise*
acostarse	*to go to bed*
acostumbrado	*to be used to*
el actor	*actor*
la actriz	*actress*
acumulado	*accumulated*
adiós	*good-bye*
¿adónde?	*where? to where?*
el aeropuerto	*airport*
afeitarse	*to shave*
las afueras	*suburbs, outskirts*
la agencia de viajes	*travel agency*
el agente	*agent*
agosto	*August*
agradable	*pleasant*
agrio	*sour*
el agua	*water*
el agua mineral	*mineral water*
el aguacate	*avocado*
agudo	*sharp*
ahí	*there*
ahora	*now*
ahora mismo	*right away*
los ahorros	*savings*
el aire	*air*
el ajo	*garlic*
al	*to the*
al final	*at the end*
al lado de	*next to, beside*
alcohólico	*alcoholic*
alegrarse	*to be glad*
algo	*something*
alguien	*someone*
algún	*some, any*
allá	*there*
el almidón	*starch*
la almohada	*pillow*
el almuerzo	*lunch*
el alojamiento	*hotel accomodations*

Spanish	English
el altar	*altar*
la altitud	*altitude*
amable	*kind*
amarillo	*yellow*
la ambulancia	*ambulance*
amueblado	*furnished*
anaranjado	*orange*
andar	*to walk*
el andén	*platform*
angosto	*narrow*
animado	*lively*
el aniversario	*anniversary*
el año	*year*
anoche	*last night*
antes	*sooner, before*
antes de	*before*
anunciar	*to announce*
el aparato	*machine*
el apartamento	*apartment*
apetecer	*to appeal to*
el apio	*celery*
aplaudir	*to applaud*
aquel	*that (over there)*
aquellos	*those (over there)*
aquí	*here*
aquí tiene	*here you are*
la araña	*spider*
el arquitecto	*architect*
arreglar	*to fix*
arriba	*above*

Spanish	English
el arroyo	*creek*
el arroyo	*creek*
el arroz	*rice*
el ascensor	*elevator*
así	*so that, that way*
el asiento	*seat*
asistir a	*to attend*
la aspiradora	*vacuum cleaner*
el asteroide	*asteroid*
atrás	*in the back*
el atún	*tuna*
el autobús	*bus*
el automóvil	*car*
la avenida	*avenue*
el avión	*airplane*
ayudar	*to help*
el azúcar	*sugar*
azul	*blue*
bailar	*to dance*
el balance	*balance (account balance)*
el balcón	*balcony*
la banana	*banana*
bañarse	*to take a bath*
el baño	*bathroom*
barato	*cheap, inexpensive*
la barbilla	*chin*
la barca	*ferry*
el barco	*ship*
barrer	*to sweep*
bastante	*rather, enough*

Spanish	English	Spanish	English
el baúl	*trunk*	el caballo	*horse*
el bebé	*baby*	la cabeza	*head*
beber	*to drink*	cada	*each*
la bebida	*drink, beverage*	la cadera	*hip*
la bicicleta	*bicycle*	el café	*coffee*
bien	*well, fine*	el caimán	*alligator*
el billete	*bill (paper money)*	la caja	*cash register*
el bistec	*steak*	el cajero	*cashier*
blanco	*white*	los calcetines	*socks*
la blusa	*blouse*	la calculadora	*calculator*
la bocina	*horn*	la calle	*street*
el boleto	*ticket*	los calzoncillos	*men's underwear*
la bolsa	*bag*	la cama	*bed*
la bomba	*gasoline pump*	la cama matrimonial	*double bed*
el bosque	*forest*	el camarero	*waiter*
la bota	*boot*	los camarones	*shrimp*
el botón	*button*	cambiar	*to change*
el botones	*bellhop*	el cambio	*exchange rate*
el bou	*type of fishing boat*	caminar	*to walk*
el brazo	*arm*	la camisa	*shirt*
el bróculi	*broccoli*	la camiseta	*undershirt, t-shirt*
bucear	*to scuba dive*	la campiña	*countryside*
buenas noches	*good night*	el campo	*country, countryside*
buenas tardes	*good afternoon/evening*	la canción	*song*
bueno	*good*	el cantante	*singer*
Bueno.	*O.K., Fine.*	la cantidad	*quantity*
¿beuno?	*hello?*	cargar a la habitación	*to charge to the room*
buenos días	*good morning*	la carne	*meat*
el bulevar	*boulevard*	la carne asada	*roast beef*
buscar	*to look for*	la carne de cerdo	*pork*

Spanish	English	Spanish	English
la carne de res	*beef*	el chocolate	*chocolate*
la carnicería	*meat counter, butcher shop*	la chuleta de cerdo	*pork chop*
el carnicero	*butcher*	cien	*one hundred*
caro	*expensive*	cinco	*five*
la carretera	*highway*	cincuenta	*fifty*
el carro	*car*	cincuenta y cinco	*fifty-five*
la carta	*letter*	cincuenta y cuatro	*fifty-four*
la casa	*house*	cincuenta y dos	*fifty-two*
casado	*married*	cincuenta y nueve	*fifty-nine*
la cascada	*waterfall*	cincuenta y ocho	*fifty-eight*
casi	*almost*	cincuenta y seis	*fifty-six*
catorce	*fourteen*	cincuenta y siete	*fifty-seven*
caurenta y ocho	*forty-eight*	cincuenta y tres	*fifty-three*
la causa	*cause*	cincuenta y uno	*fifty-one*
la cena	*dinner*	el cine	*movie theater*
el cenicero	*ashtray*	el cinturón	*belt*
el centro	*downtown*	la ciudad	*city*
el cepillo	*brush*	claro	*of course*
cerca de	*near, close to*	la clase	*class*
cero	*zero*	clásico	*classic*
cerrar	*to close*	la cobija	*blanket*
la cerveza	*beer*	cobrar	*to cash*
el chaleco	*vest*	el coche	*car*
el champú	*shampoo*	la cocina	*kitchen*
la chaqueta	*jacket*	el cocinero	*cook, chef*
la chaqueta	*jacket*	el coco	*coconut*
el cheque	*check*	el cocodrilo	*crocodile*
el cheque de viaje	*traveler's check*	el codo	*elbow*
el cheque de viajero	*traveler's check*	el cofre	*hood*
chillón	*loud (e.g. colors)*	coincidir	*to coincide*

Spanish	English	Spanish	English
la coliflor	*cauliflower*	el cuaderno	*notebook*
colonial	*colonial*	la cuadra	*block*
el color	*color*	el cuadro	*painting*
el comedor	*dining room*	¿cuándo?	*when?*
comer	*to eat*	¿cuánto?	*how much?*
la comida	*food*	¿cuántos?	*how many?*
¿cómo?	*how?*	cuarenta	*forty*
¡Cómo no!	*Of course!*	cuarenta y cinco	*forty-five*
comprar	*to buy*	cuarenta y cuatro	*forty-four*
comprender	*to understand*	cuarenta y dos	*forty-two*
la computadora	*computer*	cuarenta y nueve	*forty-nine*
con	*with*	cuarenta y seis	*forty-six*
con antelación	*in advance*	cuarenta y siete	*forty-seven*
conocer	*to know, meet*	cuarenta y tres	*forty-three*
conseguir	*to get, acquire*	cuarenta y uno	*forty-one*
el consomé de pollo	*chicken soup*	cuarto	*fourth*
construir	*to build*	el cuarto de baño	*bathroom*
consultar	*to consult*	cuatro	*four*
contestar	*to answer*	cuatrocientos	*four hundred*
contigo	*with you*	el cubo	*cube*
continuo	*continuous*	la cuenta	*bill, check, account*
convenir	*to be convenient*	la cuenta corriente	*checking account*
conversar	*to talk with, converse*	la cuenta de ahorros	*savings account*
la corbata	*tie*	el cuidado	*care*
cortarse el pelo	*to cut one's hair*	cuidarse	*to take care of oneself*
coser	*to sew*	el cumpleaños	*birthday*
la costa	*coast*	la cuñada	*sister-in-law*
costar	*to cost*	la cuota	*quota*
el coulomb	*coulomb (Physics)*	dar	*to give*
creer	*to believe*	dar clases	*to give classes, teach*

Spanish	English
de	*of*
de acuerdo	*O.K., in agreement*
de cuero	*leather*
de nada	*you're welcome*
de paso	*while you're at it*
de persona a persona	*person to person*
de ser posible	*if it's possible*
de vacaciones	*on vacation*
debajo de	*under*
deber	*to be ought to, should, must*
débil	*weak*
décimo	*tenth*
decir	*to tell*
dejar	*to leave, let*
del	*of the, about the*
delante de	*in front of*
delicioso	*delicious*
demasiado	*too much*
la demora	*delay*
dentro de	*within*
depender de	*to depend on*
la dependienta	*salesclerk*
depositar	*to deposit*
el depósito	*deposit*
el desayuno	*breakfast*
descansar	*to rest*
desde hace	*since, it's been*
desear	*to want*
desinflado	*flat, not inflated*

Spanish	English
despertarse	*to wake up*
después	*after, afterwards*
después de	*after*
detrás de	*behind*
la deuda	*debt*
el día	*day*
el Día de Año Nuevo	*New Year's Day*
el Día de Independencia	*Independence Day*
el Día de los Muertos	*All Soul's Day*
diario	*daily*
la diarrea	*diarrhea*
diciembre	*December*
diecinueve	*nineteen*
dieciocho	*eighteen*
dieciséis	*sixteen*
diecisiete	*seventeen*
diez	*ten*
difícil	*difficult*
¿dígame?	*May I help you?*
el dinero	*money*
la dirección	*address*
directamente	*directly*
directo	*direct*
la directora	*director*
el disco	*record*
discreto	*discreet, subtle*
disfrutar	*to enjoy*
disímil	*dissimilar*
el distribuidor	*distributor*
diurno	*daily*

Spanish	English
divertirse	*to enjoy oneself*
dividir	*to divide*
divorciado	*divorced*
doblar	*to turn*
doce	*twelve*
el doctor	*doctor*
documentar	*to check, document (the luggage)*
el dólar	*dollar*
doler	*to hurt*
el dolor	*pain*
el dolor de estómago	*stomach ache*
el domingo	*Sunday*
¿dónde?	*where?*
dormirse	*to fall asleep*
el dormitorio	*bedroom*
dos	*two*
doscientos	*two hundred*
doscientos	*two hundred*
dulce	*sweet*
duodécimo	*twelfth*
durante	*during*
economizar	*to budget, save*
el ecuador	*equator*
el efectivo	*cash*
el efecto	*effect*
él	*he*
la electricidad	*electricity*
elegante	*elegant*
el elenco	*cast*

Spanish	English
ella	*she, her*
ellos	*they, them*
el embarque	*boarding*
el embotellamiento	*traffic jam*
empezar	*to begin*
el empleado	*employee*
el empleado de servicio	*attendant*
en efectivo	*in cash*
en efecto	*that's correct, right*
en frente de	*in front of*
en la esquina	*at, on the corner*
en tournée	*on tour*
encantado	*pleased, happy (to meet you)*
encantar	*to love, please*
encargar	*to request*
el encargo	*order, job*
las enchiladas suizas	*chicken enchiladas*
encima de	*on top of*
encontrar	*to find*
enero	*January*
el enfermero	*nurse*
la ensalada verde	*green salad*
enseñar	*to show*
entonces	*then, so*
la entrada	*ticket*
entre	*between*
envolver	*to wrap up*
el equipaje	*luggage*
equivocarse	*to make a mistake, be mistaken*

Spanish	English
las escaleras	*stairs*
el escenario	*stage*
la escoba	*broom*
escribir	*to write*
la escuela	*school*
ese	*that (that one)*
ese	*that (nearby)*
esos	*those (nearby)*
el espacio	*space*
especial	*special*
la especialidad	*specialty, special*
el espejo	*mirror*
esperar	*to wait, hope*
la esposa	*wife*
el esposo	*husband*
la esquina	*corner*
está bien	*alright*
la estación de tren	*train station*
los Estados Unidos	*the United States*
estar	*to be*
estar de visita	*to be visiting*
estar de vuelta	*to be back*
este	*this*
éste	*this one*
estos	*these*
estrenar	*to debut*
el estudiante	*student*
la estufa	*stove*
estupendo	*fantastic, great*
el eufemismo	*euphemism*

Spanish	English
la Europa	*Europe*
evitar	*to avoid*
la excursión	*trip, tour*
el excursionismo a pie	*hiking*
extraño	*strange*
el faisán	*pheasant*
la falda	*skirt*
la familia	*family*
los faros	*headlights*
febrero	*February*
la felicidad	*happiness*
¡felicitaciones!	*congratulations*
la ferretería	*hardware store*
la fiesta	*party*
el final	*end*
el flan	*custard*
el flequillo	*bangs*
folklórico	*folkloric*
los fondos	*funds*
las frambuesas	*raspberries*
frecuente	*frequent*
el fregadero	*sink*
el fregasuelos	*mop*
los frenos	*brakes*
la frente	*forehead*
frente a	*facing*
la fresa	*strawberry*
fresco	*fresh*
frío	*cold*
la fruta	*fruit*

Spanish	English
el frutero	*fruit vendor*
la fuente	*fountain*
fuera de	*outside*
fumar	*to smoke*
la función	*show*
funcionar	*to work, function*
el garaje	*garage*
los gemelos	*twins*
gracias	*thank you*
grande	*large, big*
la grasa	*grease, fat*
gris	*gray*
la grúa	*tow truck*
el guante	*glove*
el gusano	*worm*
gustar	*to be pleasing to, to like*
el gusto	*taste*
la habitación	*room*
hablar	*to speak, talk*
habrá	*there will, it will*
hace buen tiempo	*it's nice weather*
hace calor	*it's hot*
hace fresco	*it's cool*
hace frío	*it's cold*
hace mal tiempo	*it's bad weather*
hace sol	*it's sunny*
hace viento	*it's windy*
hacer	*to make, do*
hacer camping	*to camp*
hacer juego con	*to match with*

Spanish	English
hacer la cama	*to make the bed*
hacer las compras	*to do the shopping*
hacer un viaje	*to take a trip*
hacer una llamada	*to make a call*
hacerse una permanente	*to get a permanent*
la hamaca	*hammock*
la hamburguesa	*hamburger*
la harina	*flour*
hasta	*until*
hasta allá	*to that place, there*
hasta luego	*until then, see you later*
hay	*there is, there are*
el helado	*ice cream*
el helicóptero	*helicopter*
la hermana	*sister*
el hermano	*brother*
el hielo	*ice*
los hijos	*children, sons*
la hilera	*row*
la historia	*history*
hola	*hello, hi*
el hombre	*man*
la hora	*hour*
el horno	*oven*
horroroso	*horrible, horrifying*
el hotel	*hotel*
hoy	*today*
hoy	*today*
el huevo	*egg*
igualmente	*equally*

Spanish	English
incluir	*to include*
la industria	*industry, manufacturing company*
la información	*information*
el ingeniero	*engineer*
la inmobiliaria	*rental agency*
insistir	*to insist, keep trying*
la intención	*intention*
el interés	*interest*
interesante	*interesting*
invertir	*to invest*
el invierno	*Winter*
el invitado	*guest*
invitar	*to invite*
ir a	*to go to, be going to*
ir de vacaciones	*to go on vacation*
el jabón	*soap*
el jamón	*ham*
el jefe	*chief*
la jirafa	*giraffe*
el joule	*joule (Physics)*
el jueves	*Thursday*
jugar	*to play*
el jugo	*juice*
el juguete	*toy*
julio	*July*
junio	*June*
junto a	*next to*
justo	*exactly, just*
ka	*letter k*
el karate	*karate*
el kilo	*kilogram, kilo*
el kinesiólogo	*kinesiologist*
kurdo	*Kurdish*
el labio	*lip*
el laboratorio	*laboratory*
la lana	*wool*
la langosta	*lobster*
la lavadora	*washing machine*
la lavandería	*laundry*
el lavaplatos	*dishwasher*
lavar	*to wash*
lavar en seco	*to dryclean*
lavarse	*to wash oneself*
lavarse el pelo	*to wash one's hair*
le	*to him, to her, to you (formal)*
la leche	*milk*
lejos	*far*
lejos de	*far, far from*
la lengua	*tongue*
lento	*slow*
el león	*lion*
les	*to them, to you (plural, formal)*
levantarse	*to get up*
las libras	*pounds*
libre	*free, available*
la librería	*bookstore*
el libro	*book*
el limón	*lime, lemon*
la limonada	*limonade*

Spanish	English	Spanish	English
limpiar	*to clean*	manejar	*to drive*
lindo	*pretty*	el mango	*mango*
liso	*smooth*	el mantel	*tablecloth*
listo	*ready*	la mantequilla	*butter*
la llamada	*call, phone call*	la manzana	*apple*
llamar	*to call*	la manzana	*apple*
llamar en la puerta	*to knock on the door*	el mar	*sea*
llamarse	*to be named, called*	marcar	*to dial*
la llanta	*tire*	marcharse	*to leave, go away*
llegar	*to arrive*	el marido	*husband*
llenar	*to fill*	los mariscos	*seafood*
llevar	*to take, carry*	marrón	*brown*
llevar mucho tiempo	*to take a long time*	el martes	*Tuesday*
la lluvia	*rain*	marzo	*March*
lo	*it*	más	*more*
lo	*him, you (formal)*	más bien	*more like*
lo siento	*I'm sorry*	más tarde	*later*
el lobo	*wolf*	el matrimonio	*married couple*
los	*them, you (plural, formal)*	mayo	*May*
Luis	*Louis*	mayor	*older*
el lunes	*Monday*	me	*to me*
la madre	*mother*	me	*to me*
el maestro	*teacher*	la medicina	*medicine*
mal	*badly, ill*	el médico	*doctor*
el malestar general	*general feeling of illness*	medio	*half*
la maleta	*suitcase*	las mejillas	*cheeks*
malhumorado	*in a bad mood*	mejor	*better*
la mamá	*mom, mother*	mejor	*better*
mañana	*tomorrow*	mejorarse	*to get better*
mandar un fax	*to send a fax*	el melon	*melon*

Spanish	English
menor	*younger*
menos	*less*
el mercado	*market*
la merienda	*snack*
la mermelada	*jam*
meter	*to put in*
el metro	*subway*
mexicano	*Mexican*
México	*Mexico*
mi	*my*
el microondas	*microwave*
el microscopio	*microscope*
el miércoles	*Wednesday*
mil	*one thousand*
mirar	*to look, look at*
el momento	*moment*
la montaña	*mountain*
los monumentos	*historic sites*
morado	*purple*
la motocicleta	*motorcycle*
el motor	*engine*
mucho	*a lot, much*
los muebles	*furniture*
la mujer	*woman, wife*
la música	*music*
el músico	*musician*
muy	*very*
Muy amable.	*You're very kind.*
nada	*nothing*
nadar	*to swim*
nadie	*no one*
la naranja	*orange (fruit)*
la nariz	*nose*
la Navidad	*Christmas*
necesitar	*to need*
el negativo	*negative*
negro	*black*
ni	*neither, nor*
la niebla	*fog*
el nieto	*grandchild*
ningún	*no, none*
los niños	*children*
no hay de que	*it's nothing, you're welcome*
no tener razón	*to be wrong*
la noche	*night*
la Noche Vieja	*New Year's Eve*
la Nochebuena	*Christmas Eve*
el nombre	*name*
normalmente	*normally*
norteamericano	*North American, from the U.S.*
nos	*to us*
nosotros	*we, us*
novecientos	*nine hundred*
noveno	*ninth*
noventa	*ninety*
noventa (90)	*ninety*
noventa y cinco	*ninety-five*
noventa y cuatro	*ninety-four*
noventa y dos	*ninety-two*

Spanish	English	Spanish	English
noventa y nueve	*ninety-nine*	ocurrir	*to occur*
noventa y ocho	*ninety-eight*	la oficina	*office*
noventa y seis	*ninety-six*	la oficina de cambio	*exchange office*
noventa y siete	*ninety-seven*	la oficina de correos	*post office*
noventa y tres	*ninety-three*	la oficina de información	*information office*
noventa y uno	*ninety-one*	ofrecer	*to offer*
noviembre	*November*	el ojo	*eye*
la nube	*cloud*	la olla	*pot*
las nueces	*nuts*	olvidarse de	*to forget about*
las nueve	*nine o'clock*	once	*eleven*
nueve	*nine*	la operadora	*operator*
nuevo	*new*	os	*to you (plural, informal)*
el número	*number*	el oso	*bear*
nunca	*never*	el otoño	*Autumn*
o	*either, or*	otro	*other*
la ocasión	*occasion*	el padre	*father*
ochenta	*eighty*	los padres	*parents*
ochenta y cinco	*eighty-five*	pagar	*to pay*
ochenta y cuatro	*eighty-four*	la página	*page*
ochenta y dos	*eighty-two*	el país	*country, nation*
ochenta y nueve	*eighty-nine*	el pan	*bread*
ochenta y ocho	*eighty-eight*	la pantalla	*screen*
ochenta y seis	*eighty-six*	el pantalón	*pants*
ochenta y siete	*eighty-seven*	los pantalones	*pants*
ochenta y tres	*eighty-three*	el pañuelo	*scarf*
ochenta y uno	*eighty-one*	las papas fritas	*fried potatoes, french fries*
ocho	*eight*	el par	*pair*
ochocientos	*eight hundred*	para	*for*
octavo	*eighth*	el parabrisas	*windshield*
octubre	*October*		

Spanish	English	Spanish	English
parecer	*to seem*	peor	*worse*
el parque nacional	*national park*	pequeño	*small*
la parte	*part*	pequeño	*small*
el pasaje	*ticket, airline ticket*	perderse	*to get lost*
el pasajero	*passenger*	perdón	*excuse me*
el pasaporte	*passport*	perdone	*excuse me*
pasar	*to come in, pass*	pero	*but*
pasar la aspiradora	*to run the vacuum cleaner*	la persona	*person*
pasar por	*to go through*	pesado	*heavy*
pasar unos días	*to spend a few days*	pesar	*to weigh*
la Pascua (Florida)	*Easter*	el pescado	*fish*
pasear	*to stroll, walk*	el peso	*peso*
el pasillo	*hallway*	la piel	*skin*
la pasta	*pasta*	la pierna	*leg*
la pastilla	*pill*	el piloto	*pilot*
el patio	*patio*	la pimienta	*pepper*
pedir	*to order, ask for*	la piña	*pineapple*
peinarse	*to comb*	el piso	*floor, story of a building*
el peine	*comb*	la pista	*runway*
la película	*movie*	planchar	*to iron*
el pelo	*hair*	el plástico	*plastic*
el pelo lacio	*straight hair*	plateado	*silver*
el pelo ondulado	*wavy hair*	la playa	*beach*
el pelo rizado	*curly hair*	la plaza de garaje	*garage space*
la pelota	*ball*	las plazas	*seats, spaces*
la peluca	*wig*	poder	*to be able, can*
la peluquera	*hair dresser*	el policía	*police officer*
la peluquería	*beauty shop*	el pollo	*chicken*
pensar	*to think*	el polvo	*dust*
pensar en	*to think about*	el poncho	*poncho*

Spanish	English	Spanish	English
poner	*to put*	pronto	*soon*
ponerse	*to put on*	próximo	*next*
ponerse moreno	*to get tanned*	el pueblo	*town, village*
por	*per, for*	el puente	*bridge*
por cierto	*by the way, incidentally*	la puerta	*door, gate*
por cobrar	*collect, reversing the charges*	el puerto	*port*
por Dios	*for Heaven's sake*	pues	*well*
por ejemplo	*for example*	el pulgar	*thumb*
por eso	*that's why*	las puntas	*ends of hair*
por favor	*please*	que	*that, which*
por fin	*finally*	¿qué?	*what?*
por lo general	*in general*	quedar	*to stay, remain, be*
por lo menos	*at least*	quedarle bien	*to look good on one*
por si acaso	*just in case*	quedarse	*to stay*
por supuesto	*of course*	quedarse calvo	*to go bald*
porque	*because*	Quédese con la vuelta.	*Keep the change.*
posible	*possible*	quemar	*to burn*
el postre	*dessert*	querer	*to want*
el precio	*price*	el queso	*cheese*
preciso	*necessary*	¿quién?	*who? whom?*
preferir	*to prefer*	quince	*fifteen*
preguntar	*to ask*	quince	*fifteen*
preocuparse	*to worry*	quinientos	*five hundred*
la primavera	*Spring*	quinto	*fifth*
primero	*first*	quitar	*to remove*
el primo	*cousin*	quitarse	*to take off*
privado	*private*	Quito	*Quito*
el producto	*product*	quizás	*maybe*
el profesor	*professor*	la rana	*frog*
		el rayo	*lightening*

Spanish	English
rebelde	*rebellious*
el recado	*message*
el recepcionista	*receptionist*
la receta	*prescription*
recibir	*to receive*
recibir una llamada	*to receive a call*
recoger	*to pick up*
recomendar	*to recommend*
recorrer	*to travel along*
el refresco	*softdrink*
el refrigerador	*refrigerator*
regresar	*to return*
la reina	*queen*
el remiendo	*patch*
la representación	*show*
la representación de teatro	*play (drama)*
la reservación	*reservation*
reservado	*reserved*
reservar	*to reserve*
el restaurante	*restaurant*
la reunión	*meeting*
revisar	*to check*
el rey	*king*
rico	*rich, delicious*
los rizos	*curls*
rojo	*red*
la ropa	*clothes*
la ropa interior	*underwear*
la rueda	*wheel*
el ruedo	*hem*
el ruido	*noise*
el sábado	*Saturday*
la sábana	*sheet (bed sheet)*
saber	*to know*
sacar	*to withdraw*
la sal	*salt*
la sala	*living room*
la sala de espera	*waiting room*
la sala de estar	*living room*
la salchicha	*sausage*
la salida	*departure, exit*
salir	*to leave*
la sandalia	*sandal*
la sandía	*watermelon*
el sauce	*willow*
la secadora	*dryer*
la secadora de pelo	*hairdryer*
secar	*to dry*
la sección	*section*
la sección de no fumar	*non-smoking section*
seco	*dry (adj.)*
la secretaria	*secretary*
la seda	*silk*
seguir	*to follow, continue*
segundo	*second*
seguro	*sure*
seis	*six*
seiscientos	*six hundred*
la selección	*selection*

Spanish	English
el semáforo	*traffic light*
la semana	*week*
la semana libre	*week off*
la Semana Santa	*Easter week*
la señal de alto	*stop sign*
el señor	*man, sir, Mr.*
la señora	*woman, ma'am, Mrs.*
sentarse	*to sit down*
sentarse	*to sit down, seat oneself*
sentir	*to feel*
sentirse	*to feel*
sentirse	*to feel*
septiembre	*September*
séptimo	*seventh*
ser	*to be*
la serpiente	*snake*
sesenta	*sixty*
sesenta y cinco	*sixty-five*
sesenta y cuatro	*sixty-four*
sesenta y dos	*sixty-two*
sesenta y nueve	*sixty-nine*
sesenta y ocho	*sixty-eight*
sesenta y seis	*sixty-six*
sesenta y siete	*sixty-seven*
sesenta y tres	*sixty-three*
sesenta y uno	*sixty-one*
setecientos	*seven hundred*
setenta	*seventy*
setenta y cinco	*seventy-five*
setenta y cuatro	*seventy-four*

Spanish	English
setenta y dos	*seventy-two*
setenta y nueve	*seventy-nine*
setenta y ocho	*seventy-eight*
setenta y seis	*seventy-six*
setenta y siete	*seventy-seven*
setenta y tres	*seventy-three*
setenta y uno	*seventy-one*
sexto	*sixth*
si	*if*
sí	*yes*
siempre	*always*
la sierra	*saw*
siete	*seven*
siguiente	*next*
sin	*without*
sobre	*about*
el sobre	*envelope*
sobre todo	*above all*
el sobrino	*nephew*
el socio	*colleague, partner*
el sol	*sun*
solo	*just, alone*
sólo	*only, just*
soltero	*single*
el sombrero	*hat*
el sostén	*bra*
su	*your (formal)*
subir	*to go up, get on*
sucio	*dirty*
el sucre	*sucre*

Spanish	English
suelto	*loose*
el suéter	*sweater*
el supermercado	*supermarket*
el sur	*south*
la talla	*size*
también	*also*
tampoco	*neither*
el tanque	*tank*
tanto	*so much, as much*
tantos	*so many*
el tapón de rueda	*hubcap*
la taquilla	*ticket booth*
tardar	*to take time*
tarde	*late*
la tarde	*afternoon*
la tarjeta de crédito	*credit card*
la tarjeta telefónica	*phone card*
el taxi	*taxi*
el taxista	*taxi driver*
la taza	*cup*
la taza	*cup*
el tazón	*bowl*
te	*to you (informal)*
el té	*tea*
el teatro	*theater*
el techo	*roof*
el técnico	*repairman*
el teléfono	*telephone*
el telegrama	*telegram*
la televisión	*television*

Spanish	English
el televisor	*television*
el tema	*subject, topic*
las tenazas	*curling iron*
tener	*to have*
tener calor	*to be hot*
tener cuidado	*to be careful*
tener fiebre	*to have a fever*
tener frío	*to be cold*
tener ganas de	*to feel like*
tener ganas de	*to feel like (doing something)*
tener hambre	*to be hungry*
tener miedo	*to be afraid*
tener náuseas	*to be nauseous*
tener prisa	*to be in a hurry*
tener que	*to have to (do something)*
tener que	*to have to*
tener razón	*to be right*
tener sed	*to be thirsty*
tener sueño	*to be sleepy*
tener... años	*to be years old*
tercero	*third*
terminar	*to finish, end*
la ternera	*veal*
terrible	*terrible*
el tiempo	*time, weather*
el tiempo libre	*free time*
la tienda	*store*
las tijeras	*scissors*
la tintorería	*dry cleaner's*

Spanish	English	Spanish	English
el tío	*uncle*	treinta y tres	*thirty-three*
la toalla	*towel*	treinta y uno	*thirty-one*
todavía	*still, yet*	el tren	*train*
todavía no	*not yet*	tres (3)	*three*
todo derecho	*straight ahead*	trescientos	*three hundred*
todos	*all*	trescientos	*three hundred*
tomar	*to take, drink, eat*	triunfar	*to triumph*
tomar una copa	*to have a drink*	el triunfo	*victory*
la tormenta	*storm*	tú	*you (informal)*
la toronja	*grapefruit*	los tubos eléctricos	*electric curlers*
la torta de chocolate	*chocolate cake*	último	*last*
el tour	*tour*	un	*a*
el tour organizado	*organized tour*	un par de	*a pair of, a couple of*
trabajar	*to work*	un poco	*a little*
el trabajo	*work*	la uña	*fingernail*
traer	*to bring*	la universidad	*university*
el tráfico	*traffic*	uno	*one*
el traje	*suit*	unos	*some*
la transferencia	*transfer*	usted	*you (formal)*
tratar	*to try*	ustedes	*you (formal, plural)*
tratar de	*to try to*	la uva	*grape*
trece	*thirteen*	las uvas	*grapes*
treinta (30)	*thirty*	la vaca	*cow*
treinta y cinco	*thirty-five*	varios	*several*
treinta y cuatro	*thirty-four*	el vaso	*drinking glass*
treinta y dos	*thirty-two*	veinte	*twenty*
treinta y nueve	*thirty-nine*	veinte	*twenty*
treinta y ocho	*thirty-eight*	veinticinco	*twenty-five*
treinta y seis	*thirty-six*	veinticuatro	*twenty-four*
treinta y siete	*thirty-seven*	veintidos	*twenty-two*

Spanish	English
veintinueve	*twenty-nine*
veintiocho	*twenty-eight*
veintiséis	*twenty-six*
veintisiete	*twenty-seven*
veintitrés	*twenty-three*
veintiuno	*twenty-one*
venir	*to come*
venirle bien	*to suit one*
la ventaja	*advantage*
la ventana	*window*
ver	*to see*
el verano	*Summer*
¿verdad?	*right?*
la verdad	*truth*
verde	*green*
la verdura	*vegetable*
las verduras	*vegetables*
verse	*to see one another*
el vértigo	*dizziness*
el vestido	*dress*
vestirse	*to get dressed*
el viaje	*trip*
viejo	*old*
el viento	*wind*
el viernes	*Friday*
el vino	*wine*
la violeta	*violet*
la viuda	*widow*
la vivienda	*place to live, dwelling*
vivir	*to live*

Spanish	English
el volante	*steering wheel*
el volumen	*volume*
volver a	*to return to, do again*
volver a llamar	*call again*
vosotros	*you (informal, plural)*
el vuelo	*flight*
el wafle	*waffle*
Washington	*Washington*
el whisky	*whiskey*
Wilma	*Wilma*
Wyoming	*Wyoming*
Xavier	*Xavier*
y	*and*
ya	*already*
la yegua	*mare*
yo	*I*
Yucatán	*Yucatan*
las zanahorias	*carrots*
el zapato	*shoe*
el zoológico	*zoo*
el zorro	*fox*